First Edition

# Cell Structure and Function
## Mastering the Big Ideas

BY J. Reid Schwebach

*Contributors*

Lauren Buchanan, Arba Cecia, Dana Ismail, Melissa (Mimi) Fuerst, Fareshta Jan, Athena Kalyvas, Mariam Talib, Moonisha Rahman, Lauren Smith, Yohanna Tesfaye, Tess Van Horn, and Jennifer Young.

ISBN: 978-1-63487-903-3 (pbk) / 978-1-63487-904-0 (br)

cognella® | ACADEMIC PUBLISHING

# CONTENTS

Introduction.................................................................................................v

**Chapter One**
The Study of Life...........................................................................1

**Chapter Two**
Thinking Chemically.....................................................................11

**Chapter Three**
Proteins, Lipids and Carbohydrates............................................21

**Chapter Four**
Nucleic Acids and the Origin of Life...........................................29

**Chapter Five**
Cell Theory ..................................................................................37

**Chapter Six**
Cell Membranes ...........................................................................49

**Chapter Seven**
Cell Communication and Multicellularity...................................55

**Chapter Eight**
Energetic Reactions .....................................................................65

**Chapter Nine**
Cell Respiration ........................................................79

**Chapter Ten**
Photosynthesis...........................................................93

**Chapter Eleven**
Cell Division: Meiosis and Mitosis.............................103

**Chapter Twelve**
Gene Expression......................................................113

**Chapter Thirteen**
DNA and Biotechnology...........................................121


**Appendix**
Answers to Exercises.................................................127
About the Author and Contributors............................162

# INTRODUCTION

This compendium is for use alongside a cell biology textbook, to help students learn (and help instructors teach) critical topics in introductory cell biology. At George Mason University (Mason), students are looking for simple resources and strategies to improve their learning (and their grades). The concept behind this book is to boost student performance by helping them approach challenging topics, for more efficient learning. We think this resource will save students time.

Cell biology is very eclectic, with many topics being introduced for the first time. While some students will have taken biology and chemistry, many students do not have much experience with these topics. Therefore, major points of this resource have been designed to help students focus on critical ideas so they can organize and build their understanding of *crucial topics*, be more successful in the biology course work, and be better prepared for their later course work.

This book has been written with substantial contributions from *learning assistants (LAs)*, who are talented undergraduates with experience co-teaching and tutoring other undergraduates under Dr. Schwebach's guidance. These undergraduates have a unique way of seeing how the students are learning and have been essential for this book to become what it is today. Our text has been written with crucial insight from undergraduates who have been recently challenged to understand cell biology.

Please see the photographs and introductory sentences from these LAs and student contributors in the appendix, on page 165. Our LA program at Mason is designed on the CU Boulder LA Program model (see https://laprogram.colorado.edu/) and is managed by our award-winning Accelerator Program in the College of Science (see http://stem.cos.gmu.edu/), of which I am a faculty member.

This compendium is written from experience using more than one textbook. Currently, we are using Sadava's book, *Life: the Science of Biology* (at this time, on the 10th edition), at Mason. I previously taught with *Campbell Biology*, 9th edition, and when learning cell biology as a graduate student, I used *Molecular Biology of the Cell*, by Bruce Alberts et al. (now on its 6th edition). I am a reviewer of the forthcoming 11th edition of the Sadava text. We have considered the content and methods used to explain biology in other biology books in order to create this compendium.

The chapters in this compendium take a different order than almost any text you will find. Several instructors at Mason (including myself, Dr. Reid Schwebach) teach "biochemistry" before "cell structure," with the belief that a student's understanding of metabolism and biochemical thinking allows one to obtain a deeper and longer lasting understanding of cell biology (one assumption we make with this order is that students have approached cell theory in a prior course, such as high school general biology). We have considered our students' evaluations in our cell biology course, and comments from later course work, to assess if this is a good approach, and it seems we have picked a good order of the concepts. Our Accelerator Program takes a discipline-based education research approach to understand what students are learning across courses.

This book, in addition to being a resource for students, is a resource for LAs and other instructors who are looking for a manageable compendium to cell biology texts to assist them in working with students to help them learn. To create this compendium, we: (a) reflected on how the 10th edition of Sadava aims to frame students' conceptual understandings, (b) considered how cell biology topics are presented in other texts, and (c) reflected on what students have misconceptions about and what we begin emphasizing or "doing with the students" as we help them learn.

We do not try to "do everything" with this compendium (that's what textbooks try to do); instead, we focus on what students really need to learn well. The select topics in this resource are to help students efficiently approach critical introductory topics essential for many, if not most, cell biology courses.

## ABOUT THE SCOPE OF THIS BOOK

This book doesn't cover everything in cell biology. Please use accordingly. The point is to have targeted activities that help the student learn strategically. We are targeting the critical areas that we think students need help with.

*Here are a list of parts, and a short guide, for how to use the book:*

**Introductions:** These chapter introductions are Dr. Schwebach's perspective on the content and concepts. He has written these in consultation with the LAs and students. The point is to "hear" this perspective.

**Topics Students Found Challenging:** These sections specifically address student survey responses of a large lecture section. After each test, we surveyed students about what they struggled to learn in cell biology, and importantly, we had them complete these surveys in free-response format, on sortable index cards, for extra credit. Almost every student in the class completed these surveys. Students' responses were really explicit and thought-out, since these were graded for extra credit, and students were asked just after they completed exams on the topics they responded about. We looked across the full range of students, not just the ones who came to class (who generally performed at a much higher level)! We recommend using these sections for students to consider what they are likely to struggle with, and for each student to prioritize what could be most important to "get."

**Chapter Outlines:** These are an inventory of important concepts. When studying outlines, also try to solve the Study Questions. These outlines are designed to help you organize your knowledge.

**Study Tips:** These tips are found sprinkled throughout most chapters to recommend learning strategies. These are placed next to content that could be learned more easily if the tip is followed.

**Activities, Such as Questions, Drawing Exercises and Short Answer:** One of Dr. Schwebach's LAs remarked: "I don't see the difference between the activities and the worksheets, since they both have similar questions." She continued: "Both help students test themselves to see where they are at with their learning, to know what their weak points are (where they need to work harder), and where they should focus." Exactly. In some chapters we have a more strategic plan for you. We organize problems in chapters where we think some concepts are highly likely to need reinforcement, and therefore students need to complete additional work. (Answer everything in the book. It is concise and has a workbook format.)

> *Drawing pages:* While some students may be better "visual learners," there is strong evidence that all students need to learn from a variety of different approaches. We mix instructional approaches (e.g., we also use clicker technologies, group work, pair sharing, and cold-calling students by randomly drawing note cards that identify students) in class, because students need to take different approaches to address their misconceptions and to deeply understand cell biology topics.
>
> Most students who did not like drawing at first reported on classroom evaluations that this process engages students and helps them organize what they understand. It helps students "place" their knowledge onto representations of

what they are beginning to know and helps students identify what to look up and read about; for example, when a student "doesn't know what she doesn't know."

*Worksheets:* See the "Activities" section above. We recommend using these worksheets as conversation activities (remember to talk about your written responses to the activities with your peers) with your LA or instructor. We really believe that students need to talk about what they understand, meaning the *student* needs to do the talking! (If a student is working with an LA, using this compendium, the LA should help the student give outstanding explanations by first listening to the student response, then addressing any misconceptions before providing additional information.)

**Pencasts:** You can download these for each chapter. The point for creating these is to explain core cell biology concepts to you in a clear and intelligible way that you can learn from at your own pace (see our undergraduate-authored journal publication about these, too!).[1] We credit the undergraduate Angela Shaffer, who created these electronic resources. Reid Schwebach reviewed her scripts and provided advice before she created each approximately 12-minute lesson. These resources are linked to each chapter; see the explanation about how to access and use these in the next section.

Let us know if you find this book useful and if anything would make it better. Our goal is for this compendium to help you learn efficiently, and for you to become an even better student.

Sincerely,
Dr. J. Reid Schwebach

And these LAs and RAs for cell biology at Mason: Lauren Buchanan, Arba Cecia, Dana Ismail, Melissa (Mimi) Fuerst, Fareshta Jan, Athena Kalyvas, Mariam Talib, Moonisha Rahman, Lauren Smith, Yohanna Tesfaye, Tess Van Horn, and Jennifer Young.

---

1    Shaffer, A. K., & Schwebach, J. R. (2015). Usefulness of Livescribe web recordings as supplemental resources for a large lecture undergraduate course. *Journal of College Science Teaching, 44*(4), n4.

# GENERAL ACTIVITIES SECTION

*These are study recommendations from our learning assistants. Many students taking cell biology want tips about how to study; for example, if this is their first college science course.*

- o  Set yourself up for success! This means taking advantage of your energy, schedule, and learning style.
  - o  Organize your assignments and personal life to-dos in a notebook each morning. Prioritize the most important assignment—yes, just one—for when you have the most energy. This means taking advantage of your biological prime time. Do you have the most energy to write a paper first thing in the morning, or do you find yourself more relaxed and engaged (and awake) later in the day?
    - □  If you're unsure of when your biological prime time is, spend a few days observing yourself when you study during different time of the day.
    - □  Many people find that it is helpful to tackle the most odious assignment first thing in the morning, when their willpower is the highest. Willpower has been shown to be a finite resource, and as the day goes on, you encounter numerous situations where your willpower is called upon.
- o  Take frequent breaks. If you struggle with focus and procrastination, utilize a Pomodoro Timer. Options are available to download for your computer and phone. Alternatively, you can just buy a kitchen timer and set that to 30-minute intervals. Study for 30 minutes, then take a 5-minute break. This break time is helpful to give your brain some time to refresh and help combat focus fatigue. After three 30-minute sessions, take a 20-minute break.
- o  Aim for efficiency and effectiveness. This means: Studying isn't your whole life! In his book *How to Become a Straight-A Student*, Cal Newport discusses the importance of having focused study sessions. By truly focusing during your study sessions and operating without distractions, you're able to apply 100% of your energy toward the task at hand. He explains that operating at 100% for 1½ hours enables you to get far more done effectively than operating at 30% for 3 hours. Furthermore, as stated above, your focus and willpower wane over time.

# HOW TO ACCESS PENCASTS

*Pencasts are videos that let a student click on virtual notes to study summaries of core cell biology topics. These were made by a talented undergraduate, with help from Dr. Schwebach, using Livescribe technology. Here are instructions to help you download and listen to these concise lessons:*

1.  Go to https://goo.gl/kJAin1. This is a Google Drive that contains all of the pencasts. We recommend downloading them into a folder for you to use later.
2.  When viewing and listening to pencasts, you can click on the Adobe page with your mouse and it will take you to an exact place in the notes. You can go to specific places in the notes you may only want to listen to (so you don't have to listen to everything, or you can repeat what you want to hear again).

## If you need to install Adobe Acrobat:

1.  Check and see if you already have Adobe Acrobat Reader on your computer. If you know that you do and you know how to access it, just download the pencasts and open them within the reader.
2.  If you are not sure if you have Adobe Acrobat Reader or you don't know how to open the PDF file in Adobe, follow these steps below:
    - Download the file and save it somewhere that you can easily access, such as your desktop, or a folder.
    - Go to the location where you saved it and right click the file once you have found it.
    - Scroll to "Open with" and hover over the arrow.
    - Once you hover over the arrow, a display of options should be available. If one of the options says "Adobe Acrobat Reader DC" or something similar to that, click it. This means that you already have Adobe Acrobat Reader on your computer and do not need to download it.

3.  If you do not have Adobe Acrobat Reader, you will need to download it. Follow the steps below to learn how:
    - Click on a PDF file for one of the pencasts. There should be a blue link at the top that says, "To hear or view this pencast PDF on your computer, **click here** to get the latest version of Adobe Reader."
    - Click the link "**click here**." This should take you to the direct download site for Adobe Acrobat Reader.

- Select the button "Install" to install it onto your computer, and then do as you would normally do to download an application.
- Once the download process is complete, you should successfully be able to access and open the pencast files using Adobe Acrobat Reader.

# 1

# THE STUDY OF LIFE

## INTRODUCTION

Biology is the branch of science pertaining to the study of living organisms, such as plants and animals. In this course our focus is on the building block of all living organisms, the cell. Let's begin by thinking about the origin of life. Approximately 4 billion years ago life emerged. During these billions of years, living organisms cohabitated alongside each other, allowing for Earth's biodiversity. Millions of species have been recorded, and many more are still undiscovered. The study of living organisms is essential in various fields such as agriculture, medical science, public policy, environmental science, and conservation research. The core of the scientific method includes observation, hypothesis creation, data collection, experimentation, and rejection or acceptance of the hypothesis; this method has been the base of most research studies and advancements in science.

Many students may be familiar with the topics presented in this chapter but have not yet deeply considered the mechanisms involved in scientific investigations or their relationship with cell biology. This chapter introduces the molecular origins of life and explains the process of scientific investigation, helping lay the foundation for following chapters (which are more biochemically intensive).

Full understanding of the meaning of evolution is critical. The greatest phenomenon observed in nature is the theory of evolution: the incremental, physical, and psychological changes of a species from its common ancestor have proven a fundamental principle of life. Biologists have recorded the process of evolution in various species. These findings provide evidence of modification through decent as responsible for the genetic diversity found in living populations. Many advancements we enjoy today are the result of biology. Cellular biology, anatomy, and physiology have greatly expanded our medical knowledge and understanding of how the human body functions. The applications of biology extend far beyond the scientific community into industries such as agriculture, where the study of plants and biotechnology have improved crops.

# TOPICS STUDENTS FOUND CHALLENGING

Students were surveyed just after they took an exam that emphasized the topics in this unit. The top areas these students found the most challenging are listed below.

- Difference between prokaryotes and eukaryotes (54%)
- Difference between inductive and deductive logic (36%)

# CHAPTER ONE OUTLINE

## Section 1.1: What is cell biology?

1. Biology is the area of science dedicated to studying living organisms.
2. History of Earth (see Figure 1.1).
   a. Formed about 4.5 <u>billion</u> years ago.
      i. 4 billion years ago = the origin of life.
      ii. Prokaryotes, unicellular organisms from the domains Archaea and Bacteria, emerged first.
   b. Photosynthesis began 2.5 billion years ago.
   c. Humans as we know them are only 200,000 years old.
3. What had to happen to create life?
   a. Molecules were needed to reproduce and to make other large and complex molecules.
   b. **Compartmentalization**: Groupings of molecules had to become enclosed so that chemistry could happen in a controlled and concentrated environment.

4.5 billion years ago
ORIGIN OF EARTH

4 billion years ago
ORIGIN OF LIFE

2.5 billion years ago
PHOTOSYNTHESIS

hi!
100,000 years ago
HUMANS

Figure 1.1
*Figure Source / Copyright in the Public Domain.*

    i.   This is important to know when learning about the lipid bilayer.

  c.  The leading theory today is that life originated in the ocean.

    i.   Shield from UV light and an intense, oxygen free atmosphere.

    ii.  Complex molecules in abundance, environment for chemistry to happen.

    iii. Life evolved from a common ancestor.

4.  The arrival of photosynthesis.

  a.  Key thing to understand NOW and remember for the rest of the course: Breaking down a molecule means breaking its chemical bonds, which releases energy for the cell to do work. Energy is stored in bonds.

  b.  The Earth's original environment was devoid of oxygen UNTIL photosynthesis.

    i.   See Figure 1.2 for simple refresher of photosynthesis: The main point is that $O_2$ is a result/product of this reaction.

    ii.  Cyanobacteria was likely the first photosynthetic organism.

    iii. Photosynthesis created an abundance of $O_2$ in Earth's atmosphere.

  c.  What happened to organisms when photosynthesis appeared? How did the new abundance of $O_2$ play a role in the first mass extinction?

    i.   Many early organisms died because $O_2$ was toxic to them; this is what we refer to as the "first mass extinction."

  d.  Differentiate between anaerobic and aerobic metabolism; what role did they play in early life?

    i.   **Anaerobic metabolism** does not use $O_2$ to produce energy.

    ii.  **Aerobic metabolism** requires $O_2$ in order to optimally produce energy.

    iii. The important thing to know is that aerobic reactions generate WAY more ATP (energy) than anaerobic reactions.

       1.  With more energy, cells can grow larger.

    iv. Oxygen in the atmosphere over an extended time period (2 billion years) caused

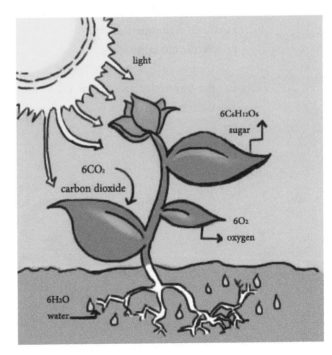

Figure 1.2

*Figure Source / Copyright in the Public Domain.*

the formation of the ozone layer, which blocked UV radiation. This allowed organisms to move from water to land.

    1. Here we begin to see the emergence of eukaryotes (uni- and multicellular organisms).

5. What role did oxygen play in the formation of life?

    a. Prokaryotes formed in the absence of oxygen.

    b. As cells were getting bigger because of new oxygen environment, eukaryotic cells were beginning to emerge.

    c. Organelles are specialized structures inside of a cell.

       i. The nucleus is an example of an organelle and is unique to eukaryotes. It holds concentrated genetic information within a protective membrane.

         1. Think of a book: All the information (DNA) is inside and the binding/cover (nuclear membrane) is protecting it from anything damaging like spills, stains, water, etc. (See Figure 1.3)

    d. What is **endosymbiotic theory**?

       i. The theory that a prokaryotic cell engulfed another cell (endocytosis), and instead of the cell being digested as normal, it became an organelle. Cyanobacteria are thought to have been digested in this manner and are known today in the cell as chloroplasts (the organelle for photosynthesis in plant cells).

       ii. Additionally, this is the official beginning of eukaryotic cells.

    e. Further development of eukaryotic cells

       i. While eukaryotic organisms today can be both unicellular and multicellular, they were first unicellular.

       ii. An important step occurred when some eukaryotic cells failed to separate during cell division. Cells were now able to grow bigger and more efficient.

Figure 1.3

*Figure Source / Copyright in the Public Domain.*

6. Phylogenetic trees are diagrams that portray similarities between organisms.
7. In naming an organism, we first identify it by its genus, and then the specific species within the genus.
8. Cellular differentiation, the process by which a cell becomes specialized, and specialization allowed for the following to form:
   a. Cell
   b. Tissue
   c. Organ
   d. Organ systems
9. **Homeostasis:** the physiological process to obtain and remain a steady state equilibrium.

## Section 1.2: Investigating life

1. Scientific investigation
   a. It is the way in which researchers and scientists use a systematic approach to answer questions based on observations or experiments.
   b. Scientific investigation is important because it raises new questions about a topic, which leads to new experimentation and in turn leads to new theories. This investigation process prompts knowledge expansion.
2. What constitutes the **scientific method**?
   a. The scientific method is a tool and a technique that allows scientific investigation and inquiry. To understand the cause-and-effect relationships in nature, use these five steps:
      i. Making **observations**
         1. Noting what one experiences using the five senses
            a. Ex.: What do I see? smell? hear? touch? taste?
         2. Making connections between different observations.
         3. Technology provides tools such as electron microscopes, global satellites, magnetic resonance imaging, and rapid genome sequences, providing greater detail and enhancing our observations.
      ii. Asking **questions**
         1. Think of questions that can help come to a conclusion, synthesize information, and build relationships as to why something may occur.
            a. Ex.: Why did this happen? What is the pattern? Would this happen in a different environment?
      iii. Forming a **hypothesis**
         1. A hypothesis is a proposed explanation to the experimental question. It is based on limited information and is testable in a scientific investigation.

      2. Looks to answer the cause or how and why something works.
- iv. Making **predictions**
  1. The predictions are the expected results or answers to the hypothesis given.
     - a. Ex.: If my hypothesis is correct ... then this and this will happen.
- v. Testing predictions
  1. Conduct an experiment to test the set hypothesis.
  2. A valid test will have a large sample, positive outcome, and be generalizable for future studies and experiments.
  3. This can lead to forming proven theories.
3. Inductive vs. deductive logic
   - a. **Inductive logic:** creating a new proposition based on the observations and facts
     - i. Inductive reasoning
       1. "IS GOHH"
          - a. Induction: Specific → General. Or, Observation → Hypothesis → Hypothesis testing
       2. The inductive process proceeds from specific observations to a general hypothesis.
   - b. **Deductive logic:** begins with a hypothesis that is thought to be true and then continues to predict what other facts need to be true in order for the hypothesis to be proved true.
     - i. Deductive reasoning
       1. "D(o)GS"
          - a. Deduction: General → Specific
       2. The deductive process proceeds from a general hypothesis to predictions about specific observations.
4. Types of experiments
   - a. There are two types of experimentations: controlled and comparative experimentations.
     - i. In **controlled experimentation**, all variables are kept constant, and only one or certain variables are manipulated to ensure that there is no influence on the manipulations. The manipulated variables are usually the "treatment."
     - ii. A **comparative experimentation** is used to determine differences between different variables or "treatments." It also compares the end result of experimentation to other sources or sample groups. In these experiments, scientists observe the differences without manipulation.

5. Statistical methods
    a. Statistical testing measures whether the differences in the experimental results are significant enough to reject. If not, the tested hypothesis result in "probabilities."
    b. Statistical tests account for the **probability** that differences in the experiment may be due to random variation.
    c. Statistical testing
        i. Null hypothesis
            1. The basis that no difference exists.
        ii. Data
            1. Quantitative information is tested and gathered in order to statistically test if the null hypothesis is correct.
        iii. Reject/fail to reject null
            1. Concludes that the difference is significant if the probability of error is less than 5%.
6. Scientific arguments
    a. Dependent on evidence.
        i. Based on reproducible and quantifiable observations.
        ii. Result in statistically significant data.
    b. Data must be must be testable and generalizable in order to be significant and useable.

# CHAPTER ONE WORKSHEET ACTIVITIES

## Study Questions

1. What is cell theory?
2. What are the two classification groups for cells?
3. How did life arise? What is endosymbiotic theory?
4. When did photosynthesis occur, and what made it possible?
5. List the characteristics of living organisms
6. What is the difference between anaerobic and aerobic metabolism?
7. What is a phylogenetic tree, and what is its function?
8. How are organisms classified?
9. How do the three domains differ from each other?
10. What is the difference between a population, a community, and an ecosystem?
11. What are some ways plants have adapted to the environment?
12. Why types of work do cells perform? Explain.
13. What is a genetic code?

14. Describe the relationship between evolution by natural selection and the genetic code.
15. What is scientific investigation?
16. What are the parts of scientific investigation?
17. What is the difference between inductive and deductive logic?
18. Differentiate between the two types of experimentation.
19. What is the difference between prokaryotic and eukaryotic cells?


# CHAPTER ONE PENCAST SUMMARY

Below is an outline of the pencast for Chapter 1. To review how to access this pencast, as well as pencasts for the other chapters, please see the "How to Access Pencasts" section in the introduction.


## Chapter One: The Study of Life

**0–3:30: Conditions for life: Early organisms**
- o  Earth is approximately 4.5 billion years old.
- o  The planet could not sustain life until 600 million years after it formed.
- o  Most of the early organisms were single celled and prokaryotic.
- o  Formation of membrane needed for these first cells to survive, in anaerobic conditions.
- o  2.5 billion years later, photosynthesis was introduced with the development of cyanobacteria.
- o  Ozone layer formed, allowing newer organisms to become aerobic.
- o  These newer organisms evolved to contain organelles, becoming eukaryotes.


**3:30–7:30: Endosymbiosis: Multicellularity**
- o  First instances began when a large prokaryote ingested a small prokaryote.
- o  Instead of breaking the smaller cell down, the two cells created a symbiotic relationship and evolved together.
- o  Mitochondria are believed to have evolved from endosymbiosis.
- o  Multicellularity occurred a little over 1 billion years ago.
    - o  Some cells failed to separate.
    - o  This caused cells to grow larger, get more resources, and adapt to various environments.
- o  About 500,000 years ago *Homo sapiens* appear.

7:30–9:51: **Shared characteristics: Evolution**
- o One or more cells.
- o The genetic information is used to reproduce.
- o They regulate the environment.
- o Extract resources to convert energy and do biological work, otherwise known as metabolism.
- o Evolution proposed by Charles Darwin and Alfred Wallace.
- o Thought that when a species breaks into two groups:
  - o They split into different areas and environments.
  - o They adapt to their environments.
  - o They become genetically different and diverse.
  - o This results in two different species.
- o Theory of evolution by natural selection:
  - o All life descends from a universal common ancestor but branches into various populations that became increasingly complex due to genetic variations that were favorable to the organism.

# 2

# THINKING CHEMICALLY

## INTRODUCTION

Atoms are the basic building blocks of life and part of the complex field of bio-chemistry, which will be introduced in the next few chapters. For the purposes of this book, we will not be considering subatomic structures smaller than electrons, protons, and neutrons. Deeper thinking about atoms will be covered in your chemistry courses.

An atom consists of **electrons** orbiting a nucleus, with the nucleus containing the **protons** and **neutrons**. The proton number is equivalent to the atomic number and is unique for each element, representing the number of protons in that element's nucleus. The sum of the number of protons and neutrons is the **atomic mass**. When an element has several "kinds" of atoms, it will have the same number of protons but a different number of neutrons; each "kind" of atom is known as an **isotope**. The radioactive nature of various isotopes is essential to production of energy, medi-cal treatment for diseases (especially cancer), and carbon dating for archeological purposes.

Atoms are held together by various kinds of chemical bonds. These bonds are vital to understand larger biological structures and shapes. For example, knowing why a molecule is positioned in a particular direction within a cell gives us greater understanding of complex structures such as lipids, and knowing how bonding con-tributes to biological principles such as solubility allows us to appreciate why some molecules dissolve in water while others do not. A **covalent bond** happens when two atoms share their electrons, while **ionic bonds** involve a complete gain or loss of electrons between two atoms. Additional weaker bonds include ionic attractions, hydrogen bonds, hydrophobic interactions, and Van der Waals forces. These bonds are extremely important to help stabilize molecules in cells. Note the **hydrogen bond** is emphasized a lot in cell biology.

**Study Tip 2.1:** Thinking chemically is a challenge for some students, and you may need to "bend" how you think. This means you will need to think about the structure and function of bonds. Making chemical models can help. Ask yourself questions like: "Will that bond rotate?" "What is the **functional group** I am looking at, and **where is the water** going to be around this molecule?" "Is the functional group able to make a hydrogen bond with water or other **polar molecules?**"

## TOPICS STUDENTS FOUND CHALLENGING

Students were surveyed just after they took an exam that emphasized the topics in this unit. The top areas these students found the most challenging are listed below.

- Difference between all types of chemical bonds (85%)
- Difference between isomers and isotopes; radioisotopes (67%)
- Central dogma (65%)
- Miller and Urey experiment (35%)

## CHAPTER TWO OUTLINE

### Section 2.1: What is an atom?

1.  Atoms are very small and are composed of a nucleus with electrons orbiting around it.
    a.  Nucleus is positively charged.
        i.  Contains protons (+ charge) and neutrons (no charge)
    b.  Electrons are negatively charged.
2.  Atoms are measured by mass (how much matter is present) and volume.
    a.  Atomic mass unit (amu)
        i.  The mass of a proton is the standard unit of measurement.
3.  The following values are good to be aware of. You don't have to try and memorize them, but think about how the values compare to one another, considering protons, neutrons, and electrons.
    a.  Weight of a single proton or neutron = $1.7 \times 10^{-24}$ g
        i.  Also called dalton; 1 dalton (Da) = $1.7 \times 10^{-24}$g
    b.  Positive electrical charge is +1 unit.
    c.  Single electron = $9 \times 10^{-28}$g = $5 \times 10^{-4}$ Da
    d.  Negative electrical charge is -1 unit.

e. Atoms have a neutral charge.
4. Key facts to remember
   a. Opposite charges attract (+/-).
   b. Like charges repel (+/+) (-/-).
   c. **Elements** are only made of one type of atom, so they are known as pure.
      i. All elements are arranged in the periodic table of elements.
      ii. Chemical symbol = identification of element
      iii. Atomic number = number of protons.
          DOES NOT CHANGE
      iv. Atomic mass = number of protons + neutrons.
          1. Can vary based on neutrons.
      v. Written convention:
          1. Symbol, atomic number lower left, atomic mass upper left.
          2. Ex.: carbon (See Figure 2.1).
   d. Main elements that make up living organisms.
      i. Carbon, hydrogen, nitrogen, oxygen, phosphorus, sulfur.
   e. **Isotopes** are formed when the number of neutrons differs from the element's standard number of neutrons.
      i. All isotopes of an element have the same number of protons; for example, carbon has two common isotopes.
          1. Elemental standard → C-12 , six neutrons in the nucleus.
          2. Isotopes → C-13 , seven neutrons ; C-14, eight neutrons.
          3. All have six protons.
   f. Elements also have an atomic weight, which is the average of the isotopes' mass based on their distributions.
   g. Isotopes are usually stable; however, **radioisotopes** are unstable and release energy freely.
      i. Radioactive decay transforms the original atom into an atom of a different element by releasing energy in the form of alpha, beta, and gamma particles.

Figure 2.1
*Figure Source / Copyright in the Public Domain.*

## Section 2.2: Chemical bonds and reactions

1. An electron's orbital is described as the space where the electron is found most frequently.
    a. An orbital can have a max of two electrons, different shapes, and different spin orientations.
    b. Elements with an atomic number greater than 2 will have electron in two or more orbitals.
    c. Electrons in the same orbital are paired.
2. Electron shells are energy levels around the nucleus, with each shell being filled by electrons in a specific sequence.
    a. First shell (s orbital): innermost electron shell containing one orbital.
        i. Filled first, lowest energy level.
    b. Second shell: contains one s orbital and three p orbitals (four orbitals).
        i. P orbitals are in a dumbbell shape and cross the x, y, z axis; hence, $p_x$, $p_y$, $p_z$.
    c. Elements with more than 10 electrons have 3+ shells.
    d. Electron energy increases the farther the shell is from the nucleus.
        i. Those whose valence shell (outermost shell) have unpaired electrons are unstable and reactive.
        ii. They react with other atoms to fill their orbitals and gain stability by sharing, receiving, or giving up electrons (octet rule).
        iii. Valence shell with all orbitals filled means the atom is stable.
3. Chemical bonds join two atoms in a molecule.
    a. Compounds are formed when two or more elements are bonded together.
    b. Molecular weight is the sum of the atomic masses of each element in the compound.
4. Types of chemical bonds
    a. **Covalent Bond**: sharing of electron or pairs of electrons between two atoms to fulfill the octet rule.
        i. Very strong bonds → require a lot of energy to break.
        ii. Single bond: a pair of electrons share (two electrons) → represented by a line between two elements.
            1. Ex.: H – H
        iii. Double bond: two pairs of electrons share (four electrons) → represented by double line.
            1. Ex.: C = C
        iv. Triple bond: three pairs of electrons share (six electrons) → represented by triple line.
            1. Ex.: :N≡N:
        v. If the same elements bond together, they share electrons equally.
            1. Ex.: C – C

      2. Ex.: :N≡N:

  vi. If different elements bond together, they share electrons unevenly; meaning the electron will be pulled closer to one element than the other, creating a dipole.

      1. Ex.: H – O – H

      2. Ex.: H-F

  vii. Unequal sharing of electrons happens because one nucleus has a greater pull on the electron.

      1. **Electronegativity**: the attractive force that the nucleus gives off on the electrons depending on the number of positive charges and the distance between the electrons

      2. The greater the positive charge of a nucleus (more protons), the more it attracts electrons. (Think of it like a magnet. More protons = larger magnet.)

      3. The closer the electrons are to the nucleus, the greater its pull.

b. A nonpolar covalent bond is a chemical bond where two atoms share a pair of electrons (equal sharing).

c. Polar covalent bonds form when electrons are pulled toward the more electro-negative element (unequal sharing).

  i. Delta negative ($\delta^-$): more electronegative atom has a partial negative charge

  ii. Delta positive ($\delta^+$): less electronegative atom has a partial positive charge

  iii. *Polar* refers to the opposite charges being at two ends of the bond.

  iv. When an electrical attraction of one atom is much greater than the electro-negativity of the other, a different type of bond forms, where one atom will lose an electron while another atom will gain that electron; this is an ionic bond.

d. **Ionic bonds** form when electrons are completely transferred from one atom to the other.

  i. When an atom gains or loses an electron, the atom forms an electrical charge and is called an ion.

  ii. Cations are positively charged ions, meaning they lost an electron.

      1. Ex.: potassium ion ($K^+$) → +1 charge shows that there is one fewer electron than protons.

  iii. Anions are negatively charged ions, meaning they gained an electron.

      1. Ex.: bromide ion ($Br^-$) → -1 charge shows that it has one more elec-tron than protons.

  iv. Ions can have multiple charges, depending on how many electrons were lost or gained.

      1. Ex.: calcium ion ($Ca^{2+}$).

    e. **Hydrogen bonds** form when strong electronegative atoms bond covalently with a hydrogen atom.

        i. Partial charges allow these formations, making them weaker that most ionic bonds.

        ii. Polar molecules are attracted to one another, and water (*hydrophilic* means "water loving"). Thus, water is a polar molecule.

        iii. Nonpolar molecules are attracted to other nonpolar molecules and not attracted to water (*hydrophobic* means "water fearing").

    f. Van der Waals forces help increase the bond of nonpolar molecules when they are close to each other, allowing them to hold together in aqueous environments (temporary bond).

5. Chemical reactions require energy so that atoms can join one another or can break the bonds that join them.

    a. In a reaction, the products will have different properties from the reactants.

6. Energy (chemical energy) is known as ability to cause change.

    a. Chemical reactions require energy to occur, yet also store energy in the bonds that are formed in the products (potential chemical energy).

## Section 2.3: Water is key

1. Water is needed for structural formation and function of all living organisms.

    a. Three states of water

        i. Gaseous state: Water molecules are spread apart and do not form hydrogen bonds with each other (water vapor).

        ii. Liquid state: The hydrogen bonds are constantly breaking and forming.

        iii. Solid state: Water molecules are tightly secured in place by hydrogen bonds (ice).

        iv. Solid water is less dense than liquid water because the water molecules are less tightly packed; hence, ice floats.

    b. For water to change to different states, energy is required.

        i. Melting: solid → liquid needs a lot of heat to break all the hydrogen bonds.

        ii. Freezing: liquid → solid releases a lot of heat because the bonds are being formed.

        iii. Evaporation: liquid → gas requires a lot of heat energy to break bonds (high heat of vaporization).

    c. Water absorbs the heat from its environment for evaporation to occur, creating a cooling effect on the environment.

2. Specific heat refers to how much heat it takes to make 1g of a substance raise by 1°C.

    a. Water has a high specific heat because of the large number of hydrogen bonds that need to break.

3. Water molecules have a lot of strength against tension because they are tightly bound through their hydrogen bonds (cohesion); therefore, water molecules at the surface are also tightly bound through those below and resistant to rupturing (surface tension).

4. Water acts as a solvent in all living organisms since many of the molecules are soluble in water (polar); these are called aqueous solutions.
   a. Acidic or basic
      i. Acids release hydrogen.
      ii. Bases accept hydrogen.
   b. pH measures the acidity or basicity of a solution based on the hydrogen concentration.
      i. pH < 7 is acidic
      ii. pH >7 is basic
      iii. pH = 7 is neutral
   c. Important quantitative concept.
      i. mole = grams of a substance or its molecular weight.
      ii. Ex.: 1 mole of oxygen weighs 16 grams.
   d. Avogadro's number = $6.02 \times 10^{23}$ molecules per mole.
      i. Used to identify the number of units in one mole of a substance; can be electrons, atoms, ions, or molecules.

# CHAPTER TWO WORKSHEET ACTIVITIES

## Study Questions

1. How do the charges of protons and electrons affect how atoms interact?
2. What is the relationship between an electron, its orbital, and its electron shells? How are orbitals and electron shells different?
3. What is the max amount of electrons located in an orbital? Does this change as the orbitals circle farther away from the nucleus?
4. Why are elements known as "pure"?
5. What distinguishes different isotopes of an element from each other?
6. Atomic weight is a concept related to isotopes. How do isotopes' varying masses relate to an element's atomic weight?
7. Are isotopes always stable?
8. Under what circumstances are isotopes not stable? Why?

## Matching

1. _____ Sharing electrons                                       A. Ionic bond
2. _____ Energy released                                         B. Isotope
3. _____ Gain/loss of electrons                                  C. Bond formation
4. _____ Energy absorbed                                         D. Covalent bond
5. _____ Difference in number of neutrons in an atom             E. Bond breaking

## Fill in the blanks

1. Acidity indicates that the number of $H^+$ ion concentration has _____.
2. The outermost shell in the orbital is called _____ shell.
3. Noncovalent attraction (bond) between a hydrogen and an electronegative atom is called _____.
4. Water-loving property is also known as _____.
5. Cations are _____ ions that are formed when an atom _____ electron.
6. A _____ helps maintain the concentration of $H^+$ and $OH^-$ concentration in a solution.
7. The ability of an atom to attract electrons is called _____.
8. The amount of energy required to raise the temperature of 1g of a substance by 1°C is known as _____.
9. Chemical reactions store energy in the chemical bonds in the form of _____ energy.
10. _____ is the number of moles of solute per liter of solution.

## CHAPTER TWO PENCAST SUMMARY

Below is an outline of the pencast for Chapter 2. To review how to access this pencast, as well as pencasts for the other chapters, please see the "How to Access Pencasts" section in the introduction.

## Chapter Two: Thinking Chemically

0–4:00: **Introduction to atomic theory**
  o   All matter is made up of atoms
  o   Three subatomic particles: protons, neutrons, electrons
  o   Isotopes: elements with different number of neutrons
  o   The periodic table

- o All the elements are grouped based on their chemical properties
- o Hydrogen is special: no neutrons (except for isotopes)

## 4:00–9:00: **Electronegativity**
- o Dipole moment
- o Tendency for nucleus of one atom to pull on electrons of other atoms is referred to as electronegativity
- o Depend on protons
- o Chemical bonds
- o Covalent bonds → strongest of the chemical bonds
- o Polar: unequal sharing of $e^-$
    - o Ex.: water
- o Nonpolar: equal sharing of $e^-$
    - o Ex.: methane, lipids
- o Ionic bonds: transfer of $e^-$
- o Ions are electrically charged particles
    - o Cations (+)
    - o Anions (-)
    - o Easily broken in water
- o Hydrogen bonds: occur between an $H^+$ on one molecule and a negatively charged atom on another molecule
- o Properties of water
    - o Water molecules join together with hydrogen bonds
    - o Understand polarity

## 9:00–11:00: **Hydrophobic interactions**
- o Hydrophobic = "water fearing"
- o Van der Waals forces are weak attractions between nonpolar molecules due to $e^-$ shift.

# 3

# PROTEINS, LIPIDS AND CARBOHYDRATES

## INTRODUCTION

Do you know the essential types/kinds of "structural" biomolecules of cells? Every living organism is made of four major classifications of macromolecules that act as the building blocks of life: proteins, carbohydrates, lipids, and nucleotides. First you need to learn about monomers. Monomers are single molecules that bind together to form polymers—large molecules with identical subunits. Many macromolecules are polymers, but not all. Macromolecules are giant molecules that consist of many atoms. Without macromolecules, no living thing could function. We will take an in-depth look at three of the four types of macromolecules and what makes them unique, how they bond, what they are made of, and why we need them.

Let's begin with proteins. Proteins are a combination of 20 different amino acids. There are four levels to a protein's structure, which will be important to know because a protein's function is dependent on its structure. The first level is called the primary structure and is the precise sequence of amino acids connected by peptide bonds. The secondary structure consists of $\alpha$ helixes or $\beta$ pleated sheets. This special folding of the polypeptide chain is the result of hydrogen bonds. The tertiary structure is what gives the protein its three-dimensional shape. Sometimes the tertiary structure will have subunits. When these subunits interact and bind together, they result in the protein's quaternary structure. Proteins have many important cellular functions, such as structural support, signaling receptors, transport mechanisms, and enzymatic roles in biochemical reactions. Because protein structure determines its function, it will be important for you to know what factors can affect or denature proteins.

Carbohydrates are the cell's source of energy. These compounds consist of only carbon, hydrogen, and oxygen. The simplest carbohydrates, called sugars, are monosaccharides and the building blocks that make up all larger carbohydrates. Monosaccharides bind together through glyosidic linkages, which form from condensation reactions. Disaccharides are two monosaccharides linked through covalent bonds. There are also oligosaccharides and larger polysaccharides. Polysaccharides can be hundreds to thousands of monosaccharides long and are commonly known as starches, glycogen, and cellulose.

Lipids are the third macromolecule we will discuss. These nonpolar hydrocarbons contain only carbon and hydrogen atoms held together by weak Van der Waals forces. The four different kinds of lipids we will cover are triglycerides, carotenoids, steroids, and phospholipids. Triglycerides are composed of 3 fatty acids and a glycerol that keep the inside of the cell separate from the outside of the cell. Carotenoids and chlorophyll capture light energy for plant photosynthesis, a process you will learn about in Chapter 10. Steroids are hormones utilized by the body to carry out chemical reactions. Phospholipids will be covered in greater detail in Chapter 6, as these lipids are what make up the cell's semipermeable membrane and play an essential role in cell function. Nucleotides are the fourth macromolecule and will be discussed in Chapter 4.

## TOPICS STUDENTS FOUND CHALLENGING

Students were surveyed just after they took an exam that emphasized the topics in this unit. The top areas these students found the most challenging are listed below.

- Differences among macromolecules (80%)
- Protein structure, especially secondary structure (76%)
- R functional groups (55%)
- Linkages involved in each macromolecule (42%)

## CHAPTER THREE OUTLINE

Section 3.1: What are the major classes of molecules in living things?
1. **Monomers** are the basic "building blocks" of macromolecules.
   a. Monomers have a functional group and an R group.
      i. Functional groups remain consistent, meaning their properties and usage will not change.
      ii. R groups determine function and bonding of the macromolecule.
2. **Polymers** are built from monomers through condensation reactions.

a. The types of bonds formed between the monomers are dependent on their R group.

3. **Macromolecules** are polymers whose molecular weight equals or is greater than 1,000.

4. **Isomers** are structures that have the same chemical composition but different atomic arrangements.
   a. Structural isomers differ in how the atoms are attached.
   b. Cis-trans isomers have a different structure around a double bond.
   c. Optical isomers: when a molecule has four other atoms bonded around it and creates an overlap in a mirror image

5. **Biochemical unity** is the concept that all living organisms are made up of the same things in the same proportions.
   a. Suggests all life has a common ancestor [see Section 1.1]


## Section 3.2: What are proteins?

1. Protein structure
   a. Proteins are made up of polypeptide chains.
      i. Polypeptide chains are the macromolecules formed when two protein monomers bond through a condensation reaction.
         1. This bond is called a peptide linkage.
         2. "Protein monomer" called an amino acid has a hydrogen atom functional group, a carboxyl group, an amino group, and an R group.
         3. Bonding structure is determined by the R group of amino acid.
   b. Levels of protein structure
      i. Primary structure: sequence of amino acids bonded to create a polypeptide chain
      ii. Secondary structure: either alpha helical or beta pleated sheet consisting of amino acids bonded together through hydrogen bonds
      iii. Tertiary structure: consists of secondary structures held together by many different types of bonds (determined by many amino acids' R group)
      iv. Quaternary structure: multiple polypeptide chains bonded together in large "clump"

2. Protein functions
   a. Enzymes: catalyze/"speed up" reactions
   b. Hormones: control physiological processes
   c. RNA: determine gene expression level

3. Protein denaturation
   a. Proteins can be broken down by:
      i. pH balance

      ii.  High temperatures

    b. Proteins can be "fixed" by chaperones (meaning properly folded).

## Section 3.3: What are carbohydrates?

1.   Carbohydrate structure
    a. Carbohydrates consist of hydrogen and oxygen atoms held together by covalent bonds.
       i.  Monosaccharides: one "simple" sugar monomer
          1.  Two forms: six-carbon (hexoses) and five-carbon (pentoses)
      ii.  Disaccharides: two sugar monomers bonded to form a polymer
          1.  These bonds are called "glycosidic bonds."
     iii.  Oligosaccharides: 3 to 20 monosaccharides bonded together
     iv.  Polysaccharides: more than 20 monosaccharides bonded together
2.   Carbohydrate function
    a. Used for energy in the body

## Section 3.4: What are lipids?

1.   Lipid structure: Lipids are nonsoluble hydrocarbons. Bonds between monomers are known as "ester linkages."
    a. Triglycerides
       i.  3 Fatty acids: A fatty acid is a nonpolar hydrocarbon with a polar carboxyl group.
      ii.  One glycerol: Glycerol has three -OH groups.
     iii.  Two types: saturated and unsaturated
          1.  Saturated: no double bond in fatty acid chain
          2.  Unsaturated: double bond in fatty acid chain
    b. Carotenoids: light-absorbing pigments, found in plant cells
    c. Steroids: vitamins/waxes
    d. Phospholipids: Three fatty acids, a glycerol, and **a phosphate group**. They are amphipathic in nature, meaning one end is polar, one end is not.
2.   Lipid functions
    a. Phospholipids make up cell membranes.
    b. They store energy.

# CHAPTER THREE WORKSHEET ACTIVITIES

## Study Questions

1. How do the three types of isomers (structural, optical, and cis-trans) differ?
2. How are isomers different than isotopes?
3. What are functional groups?
4. What is the process of dehydration synthesis (also called condensation reaction), and what is its importance?
5. What are the different functions a protein can perform in a cell?
6. What are the bonds between amino acids called?
7. What's the difference between primary, secondary, tertiary, and quaternary structure?
8. What's the importance of chaperones?
9. What's the difference between mono-, di-, oligo-, and polysaccharides?
10. What are the bonds called between monomers in carbohydrates?
11. Why is it important that fatty acids be amphipathic?
12. What's the main difference between triglycerides and phospholipids?
13. What are the four main lipid types?
14. What's the difference between a saturated and unsaturated triglyceride, and what effect does it have on the structure of the molecule?
15. Describe each macromolecule by its chemical structure and list some biological functions.
    a. Proteins
    b. Carbohydrate
    c. Lipid
16. What are the functional groups of an amino acid?
17. What's the difference between pyrimidine and purine?

## Fill in the blanks

1. Polymers of nucleotides are called _____.
2. Isomers are molecules with the same _____ formula but different _____ formula.
3. Macromolecules are generated through _____ reactions and degraded through _____ reactions.
4. Amino acids are held together by _____.
5. _____ bind carbohydrate monomers in disaccharides, oligosaccharides, and polysaccharides.
6. Triglyceride structure consists of _____ and _____.
7. A nucleoside consists of _____ attached to _____.

8. RNA is distinguished from DNA by the absence of _____, which is replaced by _____.

9. _____ are essential for the structure of a biological membrane due to its _____ property.

10. Unsaturated fatty acids contain _____ bonds, whereas saturated fatty acids contain _____ bonds.

11. Amino acids have four different functional groups attached to the central carbon: _____, _____, _____ and _____.

12. The property of amino acids (think about their N and C termini) that makes them unique is due to _____.

13. Two _____ molecules form a disulfide bond.

14. Fructose is a _____ molecule due to the presence of _____ carbon atoms.

15. The α-helix structure of a protein molecule is held in place due to a(n) _____ bond.

16. Cellulose is predominantly present in _____ cells, which is why humans cannot digest it due to lack of the enzyme _____.

17. _____ isomerism is when two molecules are mirror images of each other.

18. During a condensation reaction, water is _____, and during a hydrolysis reaction, water is _____.

19. A peptide linkage is formed between the _____ terminus and _____ terminus of amino acids.

20. Lipids are hydrophobic due to the presence of _____ bonds.

## CHAPTER THREE PENCAST SUMMARY

Below is an outline of the pencast for Chapter 3. To review how to access this pencast, as well as pencasts for the other chapters, please see the "How to Access Pencasts" section in the introduction.

## Chapter Three: Proteins, Lipids, and Carbohydrates

0:00–0:37: **Proteins, lipids, and carbohydrates**
- o Proteins, lipids, and carbohydrates
- o What is the importance of having proteins, lipids and carbohydrates?

0:37–1:06: **Monomers, polymers, and macromolecules**
- o Define monomers/polymers and how they are different than each other.

- o The structure of each compound
- o What leads to a monomer and a polymer?

## 1:07–3:36: **Structure of proteins**
- o Proteins
- o Amino acids
- o Peptide bond

## 3:37–6:23: **Structure of lipids**
- o Lipids
- o Nonsoluble hydrocarbon
- o Steroids

## 6:24–10:40: **Structure of carbohydrates**
- o Carbohydrates
- o Pentose sugar
- o Hexose sugar
- o Glycosidic bond

# 4

# NUCLEIC ACIDS AND THE ORIGIN OF LIFE

## INTRODUCTION

Do you know what the "central dogma" is? Is there really such a thing, since retroviruses exist? To answer these two questions, a student needs to understand how cellular messages and heritable information are carried by two kinds of nucleic acids and how these molecules reproduce themselves (replicate). Nucleic acids, consisting of DNA and RNA, are made of nucleotide chains linked together by phosphodiester linkages. Each nucleotide molecule consists of a pentose sugar, a nitrogen-containing base, and a phosphate group. Each living organism's genetic data is stored inside its DNA. This DNA is a double-helix pair of molecules responsible for genetic information being passed from one generation to another. The RNA will utilize that information to code for proteins. In DNA the nucleotide base consists of adenine, guanine, cytosine, and thymine. In RNA the thymine is replaced by uracil. Nucleic acids are one of the major categories of life's building blocks because of the hereditary information in DNA and the messages temporarily carried by RNA.

DNA carries the genetic information responsible for growth, development, and reproduction in all living organisms. The **central dogma** is a concept that connects important biological processes: transcription of the DNA into **messenger RNA** (mRNA) and the translation of that information into proteins, which have many important roles in cells. **Transcription** involves conversion of DNA to mRNA followed by translation of mRNA to proteins. These proteins act as building blocks that support intracellular or extracellular architectures, or are enzymes with crucial cellular functions, including tissue regeneration, catalyzing biological reactions, being a component of our immune system, etc.

Knowing the differences between pyrimidines, purines, rRNA, tRNA, and DNA is essential for you to understand how information is retained between generations of cells and how information is "expressed" as proteins.

**Study Tip 4.1:** Be sure you know these terms: pyrimidine, purines, rRNA, tRNA, and DNA. You will also benefit from drawing the structure of DNA and RNA. We will learn more about proteins in Chapter 12, which explains how translation happens.

## Topics students found challenging

Students were surveyed just after they took an exam that emphasized the topics in this unit. The top areas these students found the most challenging are listed below.

- Difference between purines and pyrimidines (56%)
- Difference between DNA and RNA structure (44%)
- Complementary base pairing (32%)
- Difference between nucleotides and nucleosides (25%)
- Protocells (20%)

## CHAPTER FOUR OUTLINE

### Section 4.1: What is the composition of nucleic acids?

1. Nucleic acids are polymers (macromolecules) of monomeric nucleotides.
   a. These polymers carry, store, and transfer some genetic information from one generation to the other. The monomers of nucleic acids consist of **nucleotides**.
      i. Nucleotides have a pentose sugar, a phosphate group, and a nitrogen-containing base. However, a nucleoside consists only of a pentose sugar and a nitrogenous base.
      ii. The nitrogenous base may be purine or pyrimidine (See Figure 4.1). If we are comparing, the structure of the purine will differ from the pyrimidine because purines have double rings while pyrimidines have a single ring.
      iii. Purine is composed of adenine and guanine.
      iv. Pyrimidine is composed of cytosine, thymine, and uracil.

### Section 4.2: What are the types of nucleic acids?

1. **DNA** is a deoxyribonucleic acid that transfers hereditary information within humans and all other organisms. Almost every cell in our body has the same DNA, but DNA does not allow the same proteins to be made in different cells. DNA is located in the

# Purines

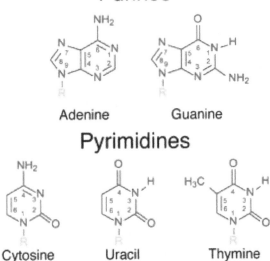

Adenine    Guanine

# Pyrimidines

Cytosine    Uracil    Thymine

Figure 4.1 Examples of purines and of pyrimidines

cell nucleus and in the mitochondria. (The information in DNA is stored as a code, and these codes are a short sequence of chemical bases, to be described in Chapter 13).

  a. DNA monomers are:

    i.  Adenine (A), guanine (G), cytosine (C), and thymine (T). It is important to know these codes pair with each other [see Section 4.3]. Nucleotides are arranged in two long strings that form a spiral called a double helix.

2. **RNA:** ribonucleotide acid

  a. There are two important ways that RNA is different than DNA:

    i.  Ribonucleic acid is a linear, single stranded polymer.

    ii.  It is composed of four kinds of bases called ribonucleotides.

• RNA has almost the same bases as DNA, but it has one code that is different: adenine (A), cytosine (C), guanine (G), and uracil (U). Uracil will take the place of thymine and bond with adenine.

  b. Like DNA, each ribonucleotide base consists of a ribose sugar, a phosphate group, and a nitrogenous base. RNA contains ribose sugars rather than deoxyribose sugars, which makes RNA unstable and more prone to degradation.

  c. The "backbone" of DNA and RNA is composed of a chain of sugars and phosphates connected together in condensation reactions to form phosphodiester linkages.

i.   The sugar is the 3' end, and the phosphate is the 5' end of each nucleotide. The way sugar and phosphate connect is by forming an ester bond between the 5' carbon of the sugar on one nucleotide and the free hydroxyl on the 3' carbon of the next nucleotide. These bonds are called phosphodiester bonds.

ii.  The sugar–phosphate backbone is lengthening in the 5' to 3' direction when the molecule is synthesized.

## Section 4.3: What is complementary base pairing?

1.  The best way to understand how each structure binds to another for both DNA and RNA is by understanding complementary base pairing.

2.  Pairs of nucleotides can bond together by hydrogen bonds between the bases.

3.  Looking at the DNA and RNA structure, we can conclude that the bases and strands of each are somewhat different.

    a.  RNA can bind with itself and may make interesting shapes like clover leaves! Note: Base pairing determines the three-dimensional shape of some RNA molecules.

    b.  DNA has (T) binding with (A) and (G) binding with (C).

    c.  RNA has (U) binding with (A) and (G) binding with (C).

    d.  Uracil and adenine are held together by hydrogen bonds; this is important because hydrogen bonds can be broken. This is really important for DNA replication, RNA transcription, and protein translation to happen.

4.  The central dogma

    a.  The two strands of a DNA molecule form a double helix and run in opposite directions of each other (antiparallel). Every human being has the same DNA molecules; however, they have different sequences of base pairs, which gives us diversity.

    b.  The following is the central dogma of molecular biology; notice the order: → DNA → RNA → polypeptide/protein.

## Section 4.4: What are the roles of DNA, RNA, and proteins in the central dogma?

1.  Lipid structure: Lipids are nonsoluble hydrocarbons. DNA can reproduce itself, and we can see that through the **replication process.**

    a.  DNA sequences can also be copied into RNA through **transcription.**

        i.   The RNA can specify a sequence of amino acids in a polypeptide through **translation.**

    b.  Nucleotide monomers have important functions for some chemical reactions and energy sources; this is the case with ATP and GTP.

2. Oligonucleotides (approximately 20 monomers) include the RNA primers, which regulate the start of DNA replication.
   a. There are many kinds of RNA in the cell, including messenger (mRNA), transfer (tRNA), ribosomal (rRNA), and small nuclear (snRNA).
3. The complete set of genes and genetic material present in living organisms is called the **genome**. Not all the information in the genome is needed for gene expression. The sequences of DNA that encode specific proteins and are required are called **genes**.

## Section 4.5: What is the molecular origin of life on Earth?

1. Scientists have conducted research indicating the need for small biological molecules to form before life could emerge. There are two theories about how life originated on Earth.
   a. Life may have originated from outside Earth.
      i. Meteorites have been discovered that contain molecules unique to life, including purines, pyrimidine, sugars, and amino acids.
2. Life began through chemical evolution on Earth.
   a. This theory states ancient Earth conditions led to the formation of simple molecules, and these molecules led to the formation of life [see Section 1.1]. Scientists have created simple molecules in the laboratory by re-creating these conditions. The products of those experiments (Miller–Urey) include organic molecules such as amino acids.

## Section 4.6: How did small molecules become polymers?

1. Large polymers arose from monomers extending themselves as chains.
   a. Scientists have used a variety of model systems attempting to stimulate the formation of polymers from monomers.
2. All biochemical reactions require **catalysts** [see Section 8.3], molecules that speed up the reactions, and from that scientists have discovered some model systems based on their assumption and observation.
3. What we understand about ribozymes and ribosome function helps validate the theory of the **RNA world hypothesis**.
   a. This is an important period in molecular evolution, because polymers are believed to have become self-replicating. There is ample laboratory evidence that this happens with RNA.
4. The unique 3-D shape of RNA allows for **ribozymes** to form, and these can have enzymatic roles, meaning they can catalyze reactions.

a. In this way, RNA seems to have acted as a catalyst for its own replication. Eventually, protein polymers were made by these ribozymes, one of the early events needed for cells to happen.

5. **Protocells**, which probably arose at a similar time as ribozymes, made compartments where ribozymes could function more efficiently.

## Section 4.7: What did the first cells look like?

1. What happens inside a cell—polymerization, catalysis, and metabolism—are special reactions that require special chemical conditions.

2. Each cell has a special cover that surrounds it called the **membrane**. The membrane is made not just for protection and the regulation of material staying inside the cell or entering it (cells need nutrients), but also to provide the perfect environment for reactions to occur inside the cell.

3. In water, **fatty acids** will form a **lipid bilayer** to form a **container** or **compartment**. Scientists refer to these first compartments as **protocells**.

   a. Small molecules such as sugars and nucleotides can pass into the protocell very easily.

4. Short nucleic acid strands capable of **self-replication** stay inside, where they replicate and repair. These strands catalyze earlier cell reactions that compose the **metabolism** of the cell.

5. How old is the oldest life we know about?

   a. In the 1990s scientists found evidence of cells in rocks 3.5 billion years old in Australia. Those cells were possibly cyanobacteria (blue–green bacteria).

   b. Cyanobacteria are aquatic and photosynthetic—they could create their own food using $CO_2$.

## CHAPTER FOUR WORKSHEET ACTIVITIES

## Fill in the blanks

6. Nucleosides are made up of _____.
7. Nucleotides consist of pentose sugar, phosphate group, and_____.
8. Nucleic acids are made up of_____ and _____.
9. Purines consist of_____ and _____.
10. Pyrimidines consists of_____ and _____.
11. In DNA base pairing, A binds to _____ and G binds to _____; whereas in RNA base pairing, A binds to _____.
12. RNA is usually _____ stranded, and DNA is _____ stranded.

13. _____ is a complete set of DNA.

14. _____ is a segment of DNA.

# CHAPTER FOUR PENCAST SUMMARY

Below is an outline of the pencast for Chapter 4. To review how to access this pencast, as well as pencasts for the other chapters, please see the "How to Access Pencasts" section in the introduction.

## Chapter Four: Nucleic Acids and the Origin of Life

0–2:04: **The structure of nucleic acids**
- o Purine & pyrimidine
- o Purine: double-bond ring
- o Pyrimidine: single-bond ring
- o Purine is composed of adenine and guanine
- o Pyrimidine is composed of cytosine, thymine, and uracil


2:05–6:50: **The origin of life**
- o Organic molecules
- o Meteorite fragments
- o Prebiotic conditions
- o Anaerobic metabolism
- o Miller–Urey's experiment
- o Ancient Earth


6:51–10:19: **Protocells**
- o Self-organized cells
- o Endogenously ordered
- o Composed of lipids

# 5

# CELL THEORY

## INTRODUCTION

The philosophical component of the evolutionary origin of life we talked about in Chapter 1 fascinates many students. What is life? It's really when a cell functions on its own and is capable of self-replication.

The cell is the fundamental unit of life present in every living organism. A major triumph to understanding life was marked by the discovery of the cell (think Robert **Hook** before **Leeuwenhoek**) and became the foundation of cellular biology. Cells are classified as either **prokaryotic** or **eukaryotic**. Prokaryotic cells are found as unicellular organisms belonging to the Bacteria and Archaea domains and are similar to the earliest cells that evolved. These cells lack membrane-bound organelles, which means they do not have a nucleus. Eukaryotic cells, on the other hand, have membrane-bound organelles and are found in fungi, plants, and animals.

All cells have a **selectively permeable membrane** that only lets certain materials move across it. The importance of this membrane is emphasized in Chapter 6. Eukaryotic cells contain various organelles responsible for their replication, including the nucleus, mitochondria, ribosomes, Golgi apparatus, the smooth and rough endoplasmic reticulum, and the chloroplast and vacuole (found in plants). Organelles have essential roles in cell growth, replication, and the transfer of genetic information to daughter cells.

Understanding cell theory will help you think out what constitutes life. Learning about **catalytic RNA** and **protocells** helps us consider how the first cells arose, beginning life on Earth. Look back at Chapter 1 to refresh your memory about eukaryotes, prokaryotes, and the origin of life.

**Study Tip 5.1:** Students reported that drawing and creating tables was an effective method to help them learn and memorize all the organelles in the cell and their respective functions.

## TOPICS STUDENTS FOUND CHALLENGING

Students were surveyed just after they took an exam that emphasized the topics in this unit. The top areas these students found the most challenging are listed below.

- Difference between cytoskeleton components (67%)
- Function of each organelle (48%)
- Difference between peroxisomes and glyoxysomes (42%)
- Prokaryotes vs. eukaryotes (23%)
- Surface area to volume ratio (15%)

## CHAPTER FIVE OUTLINE

### Section 5.1: What is cell biology?

1. **Cell theory** explains the value of cells to all of biology. All living organisms are composed of cells, and life would not have occurred without these important structures. Cells grow, reproduce, and allow for the transport of materials across their cell membrane.
   a. **Cell theory features**
      i.   Cells are the fundamental units of life.
      ii.  All organisms are composed of cells.
      iii. All cells come from preexisting cells.
2. Important details about the **composition of the cell**
   a. **Major components** include water and small and large molecules. These components are able to provide energy for the cell.
   b. Knowing about the **size of the cell**
      i.   Understanding **surface area to volume ratio:** As an object grows larger, its volume increases faster than its surface area.
      ii.  Cells must maintain a **large** surface area to volume ratio in order to function. (One reason: Metabolic enzymes catalyze reactions within and across these surfaces.)
3. **Microscopy:** an important set of techniques used in observing cells and proven to be a valuable skill in cell biology–related endeavors.

a. Cells are very small and cannot be seen by the naked eye. Usually, their size is approximately 1 to 100 micrometers.

b. In order to visualize the cells, we will need to comprehend two important things.

   i. **Magnification:** to increase the visible size of the cell.

   ii. **Resolution:** allows the user to distinguish between two points that are imperceptibly close.

c. There are two major types of microscopy

   1. **Light microscope:** uses visible light and magnifying lenses to examine small objects not visible by the naked eye. Light microscope is unique because it can visualize **living things**.

   2. **Electron microscope (EM):** a microscope with high magnification and resolution. It can only visualize **dead cells**. The electron microscope branches out to:

     a. Scanning electron microscope (**SEM**): allows us to picture the surface of a specimen.

     b. Transmission electron microscope (**TEM**): allows us to picture the internal structure of specimen.

d. **Freeze fracture** allows a researcher to see along the cell membrane and understand what is visible on the inside of the membrane. For this technique the cells are first frozen, then sliced using a thin knife.

4. **The plasma membrane**

a. Cells would not be able to function without having the plasma membrane, the outer surface of every cell (which may lie beneath a cell wall). See Section 6.1.

b. The plasma membrane can only be seen by the electron microscope.

c. It is composed of a phospholipid bilayer and has other materials, including proteins and carbohydrates, that are embedded within it and peripheral to it.

5. **The function of the plasma membrane**

a. Is a **selectively permeable** barrier, meaning only specific materials are allowed to enter.

b. Allows the cell to maintain a constant internal environment (**homeostasis**).

c. Allows **communication between cells**, including the receiving of signals. Cell migration can also happen, involving proteins that are binding and adhering to adjacent cells (see Section 6.4).

6. Cells are classified either as **prokaryotic** or **eukaryotic**.

a. **Prokaryotic** cells do not have a nucleus or membrane-enclosed internal compartments; life-forms include **Bacteria** and **Archaea**.

b. **Eukaryotic** have a nucleus (with DNA) and membrane-enclosed compartments; life-forms include **plants, fungi, and animals**.

## Section 5.2: Prokaryotic cells

1. Pay close attention to the structure so that you can compare it with eukaryotic cells.

**Study Tip 5.2:** Use the diagrams in this chapter for your own study and conduct your own concept inventory about cells; label and color the diagrams to ensure you can identify the cell features and parts. Use the lists in this outline as an inventory of what you should know.

2. Details to know about prokaryotic cells
   a. The size of prokaryotic cells ranges from 1 to 10 micrometers.
   b. Note that all prokaryotic cells have the same features, including:
      i. **Nucleoid:** DNA is contained in a region.
      ii. **Cytoplasm:** consists of cytosol (liquid component) plus filaments and particles
         1. **Cytosol:** water with dissolved ions and soluble macromolecules
      iii. **Ribosomes:** A mixture of RNA and protein
      iv. Cell wall/peptidoglycan
         1. Some bacteria have a slimy **capsule** that is made by polysaccharides.
      v. **Outer membrane:** a lipid bilayer
      vi. NO ORGANELLES!!
      vii. Some prokaryotes have **cilia** and **flagella** for movements. Both cilia and flagella are made of proteins.
         1. Cilia: hair-like structure. Bacteria can have both motile and nonmotile cilia.
         2. Flagella: Made of protein called **flagellin**. Prokaryotic flagella spin and rotate when moving.

## Section 5.3: Characteristics of eukaryotic cells

1. Comparing eukaryotic cells to prokaryotic cells, you will see similarities and differences. Eukaryotes are more complex.

**Study Tip 5.3:** Make **a list of animal and plant cell components**; use your textbook to write out the role of each item. Use the table in your study questions at the end of this chapter.

2. Details to know about eukaryotic cells
   a. **Eukaryotes** are cells with membrane-enclosed compartments called **organelles**.

  i. Organelles have important roles. For example, chloroplasts and mitochondria make metabolic products, which can be converted into molecules that "power" cell function and maintain the composition of the cell.

  ii. The DNA is located in the nucleus.

 b. Here is a list of important items found in **ALL eukaryotic cells**.

  i. **Nucleus:** a double membrane that holds the genetic information of a cell

   1. **Nuclear envelope:** the double-layered membrane (meaning two lipid bilayers) that encloses the nucleus.

   2. **Chromatin:** the material that composes chromosomes; consists of protein, RNA, and DNA.

   3. **Nuclear lamina:** regulates DNA replication and cell division.

  ii. **Mitochondria:** where the majority of cellular respiration and energy production occurs.

  iii. **Ribosomes:** Found in both eukaryotes and prokaryotes, they synthesize protein throughout the cell. They can be found floating freely or attached to the endoplasmic reticulum.

  iv. **Endomembrane system**

   1. Includes the nucleus.

   2. **Rough endoplasmic reticulum** is called rough ER (RER) because of the ribosomes located on its membrane.

   3. **Smooth endoplasmic reticulum** does not contain ribosomes. Smooth ER (SER) is the location of steroid synthesis.

   4. **Golgi:** "FedEx. Shipping and Receiving center."

    a. **Cis:** side facing the nucleus.

    b. **Trans:** side faces outer membrane.

   5. **Primary lysosomes:** used for digesting material in other **vesicles**.

   6. **Secondary lysosomes:** Second stage of cell's digestion of material. Note the fusion of a primary lysosome with a phagosome.

  v. **Peroxisomes** collect and break down toxic by-products of metabolism such as $H_2O_2$, using specialized enzymes.

**Study Tip 5.4:** Draw the endomembrane system and label every part using the terms above. Address how the cell digests food using phagocytosis, how the cell transports newly synthesized proteins to the surface, and what role the nuclear lamina plays in items coming into and out of the nucleus.

## Section 5.4: Characteristics of eukaryotic plant cells

1. Details to know about eukaryotic plant cells: The following are in addition to Section 5.3, since plant cells have all those features and also have the features listed here in Section 5.4.

    a. **Plastids:** a class of organelles that includes chloroplasts, amyloplasts, and chromoplasts.
    
        i. **Chloroplasts:** Make sure you know the role of the **internal membranes** and what **granum, stroma,** and **thylakoids** are. If you have learned about the biochemistry of **photosynthesis,** your knowledge should connect here. What is the role of these chloroplast features for photosynthesis to happen? If you need help with photosynthesis, refer to Chapter 10.
        
        ii. **Chromoplasts:** e.g., gives flowers color to attract pollinators
        
        iii. **Amylosplasts** store starches.
    
    b. **Glyoxysomes:** Lipids are converted to carbohydrates for growth.
    
    c. **Vacuoles** are important in maintaining plant cell size and **turgor pressure** (general cell internal pressure). They also have a critical role in storing metabolites, waste products, and water.
    
        i. Contractile vacuoles: pump water and waste out of protist cells to maintain concentration.
        
        ii. Central vacuole: maintains plants' shape and structure.
        
        iii. Food vacuole: stores the food for the plant.
    
    d. The plant cell wall.
    
        i. Surrounds the plant cell and is made of cellulose.
        
        ii. Provides strength, rigidity, and protection to the cell interior.
        
        iii. Only found in plants.
    
    • **Plasmodesmata:** These have a role similar to gap junctions [See Section 6.2]. Small molecules can make it across the cell wall, between plant cells.

**Study Tip 5.5:** Make a full-page drawing of the chloroplast; it is important for you to compare your chloroplast drawing to your mitochondria drawing. The authors and contributors of this book note that our cell biology course evaluations have shown this to be a powerful approach to learning the large amount of information included in cell biology and boosting your grade.

## Section 5.5: Other crucial things to know about eukaryotic cells

1. For ALL kinds of eukaryotic cells, e.g. both plant and animal cells:

    a. **The cytoskeleton:** Eukaryotic cells have different kinds of structures that help the cell maintain its shape and internal organization. The cytoskeleton has many important functions, including:

i. Movement of organelles within the cell.

ii. Movement of the organism.

iii. Involved in cytoplasmic streaming.

iv. Interacts with extracellular structures to hold the cell in place.

v. Maintaining the cell shape and internal organization.

b. There are several components of the **cytoskeleton.**

i. Microfilaments

1. Made from the **protein actin.** Actin has positive (+) and negative (−) ends and polymerizes to form long helical chains.

2. **Actin filaments** can be associated with a "**motor protein**" such as myosin. The interactions between actin and myosin lead to the muscle contraction.

3. These can help cells move (e.g., **pseudopods**).

ii. **Intermediate filaments.**

1. It is made of many different kinds of molecules.

2. It is a tough, ropelike protein assemblage.

3. It can anchor an extensive cell structure (e.g., intestinal cells).

iii. **Microtubules.**

1. Long, hollow cylinders, it acts as a framework. It is made of the protein **tubulin**—a dimer.

2. Has positive (+) and negative (−) ends.

3. The length of microtubules can change by adding or breaking dimers [see Section 11.2].

2. How do both **prokaryotic and eukaryotic cells move?**

a. Can single animal eukaryotic cells move? We are talking about amoeba, for example. **Cilia** and **flagella** are responsible for movement in eukaryotic cells. Complex animals (like humans) do not have somatic (body) cells that move like this, but cilia are important for the movement of cells in the intestine. Other animal cells, especially immune cells, are able to move into tissues and bone through the lymphatic system.

b. Do prokaryotes move the same way? Yes. They use cilia and flagella.

c. **Cilia** and **flagella** are made of microtubules in "9 + 2" array.

i. "9 + 2": nine microtubules surrounding a central single microtubule

ii. **Cilia:** shorter than flagella, and many cilia usually work together. These move with two strokes: stiff power stroke and flexible recovery stroke.

iii. **Flagella:** longer than cilia, "snakelike movement," usually no more than two present.

iv. The movement of cilia and flagella results from the sliding of the microtubule doublets. The doublets are also connected. This movement would not occur without dynein and nexin.

1. **Dynein** binds to microtubule doublets and allows them to slide past each other.
2. **Nexin** cross-links the doublets and prevents them from sliding, and the cilium bends.
3. An example to know: The motor protein **kinesin** moves vesicles or organelles from one part of a cell to another.
   a. It first binds to a vesicle and moves it along by changing the shape.
   b. This movement is driven by ATP hydrolysis.

3. **The function of the extracellular structures:** The majority of tissue volume is made up of extracellular space.
   a. This is really a eukaryotic concept; however, prokaryotes are likely to make bio-films that have similar roles for communities of microbes. The rest of this section focuses on eukaryotes.
   b. The **extracellular matrix**, made up of water, minerals, **proteoglycans**, and **fibrous proteins**, is responsible for determining how the tissue looks and how it functions.
      i. The components of this matrix are produced and organized by cells that live within it.
      ii. It plays an important role in the formation of new cells and important extracellular structures; e.g., bone.
      iii. It assists **communication between cells**; e.g., for animal cells.

## Section 5.6: The origin of eukaryotic cells

1. There are a few critical things to know with respect to how eukaryotic cells originated about **1.5 billion years ago**.
   a. An important detail of eukaryotes is how internal structures formed.
      i. Evidence points to the endomembrane system evolving to encapsulate DNA and **form the nucleus.**
      ii. Research evidence shows us that symbiotic cells currently exist (e.g., amoeba internalize and sustain some bacteria), and it is likely that cells internalized and maintained once-separate prokaryotic cells.
         1. **Endosymbiotic theory:** This theory states that organelles (e.g., the chloroplast and mitochondria) were once independent prokaryotic cells before becoming internalized to become what we now know as eukaryotes.

# CHAPTER FIVE WORKSHEET ACTIVITIES

## Study Questions

1. What is the importance of a cell's surface area to volume ratio?
2. What are the main functions of a microscope?
   a. Describe the difference between a light and electron microscope.
   b. Follow up: True/False the plasma membrane is best seen with a light microscope.
3. Explain the composition of the plasma membrane and its importance to the cell.
4. Fill out the table (✓) for what structures are found in prokaryotic and eukaryotic cells.

| STRUCTURE | PROKARYOTE | EUKARYOTE |
| --- | --- | --- |
| plasma membrane | | |
| nucleus | | |
| nucleoid | | |
| ribosomes | | |
| cytoplasm | | |
| cytosol | | |
| cell wall | | |
| cytoskeleton | | |
| mitochondria | | |
| endoplasmic reticulum | | |
| flagella | | |
| pilli | | |
| cilia | | |

5. What specialized cell structures are specific to plants? Explain their functions.

# CHAPTER FIVE PENCAST SUMMARY

Below is an outline of the pencast for Chapter 5. To review on how to access this pencast, as well as pencasts for future chapters, please refer back to the introduction and read the instructions.

## Chapter Five: Cell Theory

**0–1:75: Blood vessels: leukocytes**
- Infection/inflammation that happens inside or outside of the blood
- Protein strands
- Blood flow
- Leukocytes are close to the endothelial cells

**1:76–2:57: Purple and yellow protein strands**
- Extracellular matrix of leukocytes and endothelial cells

**2:57–3:37: Plasma membrane structure**
- Fluid mosaic model
- Protein embedded inside and out

**3:37–6:28: Cytoskeleton**
- Microfilament
- Actin filaments
- Microvilli
- Spectrin protein

**6:29–7:56: Microtubule and motor proteins**
- Change shapes
- Kinesin transports vesicles across microtubules. The movements are toward the (+) end.
- Dinen protein
  - Movement of cilia
  - Attach between two microtubules; when it moves it causes the microtubules to slide next to each other

7:57–11:39: **Organelles**
- o Mitochondria
- o Centrosome of centrioles
- o Nuclear envelope
  - o Protection of nucleus
- o Ribosome protein synthesis in the interior of the ER
  - o Protein leaves the ER
- o Golgi apparatus
- o Vesicle fusion of plasma membrane

# 6

# CELL MEMBRANES

## INTRODUCTION

In this chapter we will think about cell compartments, with cell membranes making up the exterior of these containers. Some items can cross this barrier, others cannot. To better grasp the concept of a membrane, imagine a ziplock bag. Some air will get in through tiny passage points, but for the most part nothing large can get in or out without first opening the bag. Consider all functions the outer cell membrane needs to perform: It needs to regulate the transfer of material across it, keep a stable pressure (turgor pressure if inside a plant cell) so as not to burst, and interact with the external environment. Many mechanisms are in place to help it perform these tasks, which will be covered in this chapter. We will also discuss the components of the membrane and the organization of the membrane itself.

The cell membrane has two important portions, primarily the hydrophilic and hydrophobic regions. **Hydrophilic** (water-loving) heads are electrically charged and happy to interact with the polar water molecules. For this reason, they make up the exterior of the cell membrane. **Hydrophobic** (water-hating) lipid tails are repelled by water and therefore can be found on the inside of the cell membrane. Think of a peanut butter and jelly sandwich. The hydrophilic heads of the membrane are the two pieces of bread, and they interact with your hand or, in the case of the cell, the water. The hydrophobic tails are the peanut butter and jelly, and they are on the inside of the sandwich because, just like you don't want jelly all over your hands, the hydrophobic tails and the water don't want to interact either.

The cell membrane does a fantastic job determining what can and cannot enter the cell. There are several mechanisms it uses to do this: **active transport**, being the transport of materials against their concentration gradient; and **passive transport**, being the transport of materials along their concentration gradient. To understand these mechanisms, we will discuss terms including *hypertonic, isotonic,* and *hypotonic,* as well as *concentration gradient, diffusion,* and *osmosis.* Beginning with channel proteins, which exist on the cell membrane to assist in transport of molecules, this class (kind) of protein is known as either **gated channel proteins** or **carrier proteins,** engaged in either active primary or active secondary transport mechanisms. Scattered throughout the membrane are peripheral and integral membrane proteins, which will be discussed in detail as we progress through the chapter.

We will learn about cell recognition and adhesion as we discuss how cell molecules on the exterior and even the interior of the cell allow for cell movement (migration) and bonding. Cellular bondings, otherwise called cell junctions, come in three forms: tight junctions, desmosomes, and gap junctions. The details of these junctions, including their actin filaments and other kinds of filaments in the cell-like microtubules, give them added strength. Integrin, a protein that can bind to the extracellular matrix (ECM), allows cells to move.

## TOPICS STUDENTS FOUND CHALLENGING

Students were surveyed just after they took an exam that emphasized the topics in this unit. The top areas these students found the most challenging are listed below.

- Protons moving through ion channels against the concentration gradient and carrier proteins (70%)
- Difference between passive and active transport (58%)
- Osmosis (hypertonic vs. isotonic vs. hypotonic solutions) (45%)
- Fluid mosaic model (30%)
- Cell junctions, such as tight junctions, desmosomes, and gap junctions (25%)

## CHAPTER SIX OUTLINE

### Section 6.1: What is a biological membrane?

1. Cell membranes are made of **amphipathic** phospholipids.
   a. The hydrophilic "heads" point outward, while the hydrophobic tails face inward.
   b. Two rows of these line up tail-to-tail to create a bilayer.
   c. Temperature can influence the fluidity of the membrane.
2. Membrane proteins are protein receptors within the membrane.
   a. **Peripheral proteins** lack exposed hydrophobic groups and therefore do not penetrate the bilayer. They remain on one side of the bilayer.

b. **Integral proteins** have hydrophobic and hydrophilic regions. They penetrate the bilayer.
   i. Transmembrane proteins are integral proteins that extend across the bilayer.
3. **Membrane-bound carbohydrates:** Membranes contain carbohydrates that serve as signals for other cells or molecules.
   a. **Glycolipids** are carbohydrates bonded to lipids.
   b. **Glycoproteins** are carbohydrates bonded to proteins.

**Study Tip 6.1:** Draw and label the phospholipid bilayer using bright colors. The colors will help increase association between names, locations, and functions of the different components. Be sure to include the different types of membrane proteins and know which components are responsible for moving the cell and which are responsible for the diffusion of particles in and out of the cell.

## Section 6.2: How are substances actively moved across a membrane?

1. **Active transport:** movement of molecules across the cell membrane requiring energy.
   a. Active transport direction
      i. **Uniporter** moves one substance in one direction.
      ii. **Symporter** moves two substances in the same direction.
      iii. **Antiporter** moves two substances in opposite directions.
   b. **Primary active transport** requires direct use of ATP.
      i. **Sodium/potassium pump:** antiporter that brings two potassium ions into the cell for every three sodium ions out.
   c. **Secondary active transport:** derives energy from concentration gradient established during primary active transport.
      i. Means the efforts of two membrane proteins are coupled.

## Section 6.3: How are substances passively transported across a membrane?

2. **Selective permeability:** Cell membranes allow some substances into the cell and not others.
   a. **Passive transport** doesn't require energy for a molecule or ion to enter or exit across a cell membrane.
      i. **Concentration gradient:** In passive transport, the movement of molecules depends on the concentration gradient. Equilibrium demands there be an equal balance of molecules on either side of the cell membrane. Molecules will move from high concentration to low concentration across the cell membrane.

ii. **Diffusion** is the movement of a molecule across the membrane, along its concentration gradient toward equilibrium. The speed of this process is influenced by temperature, charge, and size of molecules.
1. **Simple diffusion:** process by which small nonpolar molecules move across the membrane toward equilibrium.
2. **Facilitated diffusion:** movement of polar molecules.
   a. **Channel proteins:** integral membrane proteins that form a channel for ions
      i. **Ion channels:** channel proteins with hydrophilic pores, allowing for opening or closing of the channel with chemical signals (**ligands**).
   b. **Carrier proteins:** proteins that bind to ions to assist their movement across the membrane.
3. **Osmosis:** movement of <u>water</u> across concentration gradient
   a. **Hypertonic:** higher solute concentration
   b. **Isotonic:** equal solute concentration
   c. **Hypotonic:** lower solute concentration
   d. **Aquaporins:** special water channels on the cell membrane

## Section 6.4: What is the role of the plasma membrane in cell adhesion and recognition?

1. **Cell recognition:** how cells recognize glycoproteins to engage in adhesion.
   a. **Homotypic:** The same glycoprotein sticks out from both of the cells that are about to bond.
   b. **Heterotypic:** Different glycoproteins stick out from either cell.
2. **Cell adhesion:** how the cells bond
   a. **Tight junctions** allow for controlled movement of molecules around a layer of cells.
   b. **Desmosomes** act as "weld spots," areas of extremely close junction.
   c. **Gap junctions** allow for communication between cells.
      i. These allow small molecules to pass between cells.
   d. **Extracellular matrix:** Cells also bond to the extracellular matrix through trans-membrane proteins called integrin.

## Section 6.5: What is endocytosis and exocytosis?

1. **Endocytosis:** The cell membrane forms a vesicle around the molecule and brings it into the cell.

a. **Receptor-mediated endocytosis:** Glycoproteins bind to molecule to form vesicle.

   i. Have clathrin-coated "pits" in the vesicle

b. **Exocytosis:** Membrane forms a vesicle, a molecule inside the cell, and moves it out.

c. **Phagocytosis:** "Eating" a molecule. The cell membrane engulfs the molecule and brings it inside the cell.

d. **Pinocytosis:** "Gulping" a liquid substance. The cell membrane engulfs liquid and brings it inside the cell.

# CHAPTER SIX WORKSHEET ACTIVITIES

## Study Questions

1. Why would glycoproteins and glycolipids be important in immune responses?
2. Do peripheral proteins depend on integral proteins?
3. What is the function of each cell junction type?
4. Is the sodium–potassium pump a uniporter, symporter, or antiporter?
5. Does cell adhesion depend on cell recognition? How?
6. What is the importance of selective permeability?
7. What is the goal of diffusion?
8. How do diameter, temperature, and concentration gradient dictate how quickly diffusion can occur?
9. What would the cell look like if it were hypertonic, isotonic, or hypotonic?
10. What's the relationship between channel proteins and carrier proteins? Are they separate forms of the same process or codependent?
11. How do gated channels contribute to cell communication?
12. How do primary active transport and secondary active transport differ in their energy sources?

# CHAPTER SIX PENCAST SUMMARY

Below is an outline of the pencast for Chapter 6. To review how to access this pencast, as well as pencasts for future chapters, please refer back to the introduction and read the instructions.

## Chapter Six: Cell Membranes

**1:00: Phospholipid bilayer**
- Membranes made from bilayer of phospholipids
- Atoms can pass, and nonpolar molecules can pass.
- Glucose/ions cannot pass the bilayer.
- Has hydrophilic head and hydrophobic tail

**6:00: Passive transport**
- No metabolic energy is used.
- Osmosis: diffusion of $H_2O$ molecules down a concentration gradient
  - Form of diffusion
- Facilitated diffusion
  - Channel proteins
    - $K^+$ channels
    - Aquaporin: channel proteins that regulate flow of $H_2O$ in cells
  - Carrier proteins: can reach maximum diffusion rate due to saturation

# 7

# CELL COMMUNICATION AND MULTICELLULARITY

## INTRODUCTION

Cells are constantly challenged with a barrage of information and have to interpret these "**signals**" to determine if the cell should respond. Cells respond to signals that come from nearby locations (e.g., nerve to nerve) and from faraway places (e.g., **hormones**). For example, in a human, signaling systems are both local and distant. When a signal contacts a cell, it can temporarily and "reversibly" bond to a receptor. If this triggers a cell response, it will activate signal transduction pathways.

The events start with the molecule (**ligand**) binding the receptor, causing the receptor to undergo conformation changes (the receptor changes shape after ligand binding), followed by later events (**signal transduction**), causing both short-term and long-term changes in the cell. All of this is part of cell communication, which helps us understand how cells react to signals.

The protein kinase cascade is an important cellular response that will amplify a signal. Receptor activity can be complicated, with more than one receptor engaging to initiate a cell response. The communication needed for this function is known as **crosstalk**. **Second messengers** play vital roles in signaling pathways. A few second messengers we will cover and you will want to be aware of are calcium ions ($Ca^{2+}$), nitric oxide (NO), cyclic AMP (cAMP), DAG, and $PIP_2$.

# TOPICS STUDENTS FOUND CHALLENGING

Students were surveyed just after they took an exam that emphasized the topics in this unit. The top areas these students found the most challenging are listed below.

- G protein coupled receptors (88%)
- $PIP_2$ hydrolysis (87%)
- Protein kinase receptors (65%)
- The concept of second messengers; all their functions (60%)
- Binding of receptors to ligands (45%)
- $K_D$ (40%)
- Crosstalk (25%)

# CHAPTER SEVEN OUTLINE

## Section 7.1: How do cells respond to signals?

1. Signal → receptor → effects inside cells
   a. Signals can come in many different forms, such as stimuli like light, though we will most often talk about **ligands** (molecules) as signals.
   b. Receptors are proteins that receive these signals, or ligands.
      i. Some are in the outer membrane of the cell, while some are on the inside of the cell.
   c. Imagine this: In a game of baseball, the ligand is the ball, the receptor the glove, and the reaction of the crowd is the cellular effect.
2. Different types of signals to know
   a. **Autocrine:** a cell signals to self
   b. **Juxtacrine:** a cell signals to an adjacent cell
   c. **Paracrine:** a cell signals to nearby cells
   d. **Endocrine:** a cell signals very far to distant areas in the body (hormones)
3. What is $K_D$ and what does it have to do with ligands and receptors?
   a. $K_D$ is the dissociation constant of a receptor and is a measure of how well a receptor binds to a ligand.
   b. A low $K_D$ means the receptor is able to bind tightly to the ligand even when the ligand concentration is low.
   c. When $K_D$ is high, the receptor requires a higher concentration of ligand for it to bind. So the receptor does not bind to the ligand well.
   d. Receptors can have inhibitors like enzymes can; look to Chapter 8 to make this comparison.

4. Types of receptors to know and understand.
   a. **Ion channel receptors** (See Figure 7.1)
      i. Opening of a gate in a cell that allows ions through (Ligands shown by arrows on Left of Figure 7.1)
         1. Ions can't otherwise enter the cell, because they're too big and have an an electric charge, so they can't pass through the membrane.
         2. Think of a large ship passing a bridge; it may need a drawbridge (ion channel), otherwise it couldn't pass.
      ii. An example of this is **acetylcholine**; this is explained further in the next section.

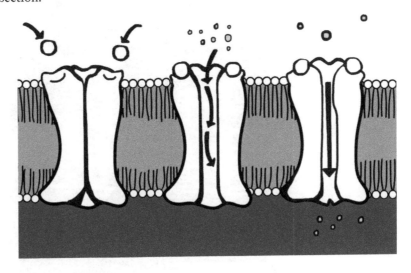

Figure 7.1 Ion Channel

   b. **G protein–linked receptors** (See Figure 7.2)
      i. A G protein is a type of protein made of three subunits.
      ii. When a g protein binds to a receptor, it activates and causes GTP to change, or hydrolyze, into GDP, giving energy to and activating an effector protein, causing a cellular response.
   c. Intracellular receptor
      i. These receptors are inside the cell, not in the membrane.
      ii. Molecules that activate this receptor will be nonpolar, meaning they can cross a lipid bilayer in order to get to the receptor.
      iii. An example of this type is the **cortisol** receptor; a cortisol receptor is normally bound to a **chaperone protein** inside the cell, making it too large to enter the nucleus. However, with cortisol (a ligand) bound to the receptor, the chaperone releases the cortisol receptor, and it can enter the nucleus to perform its job.

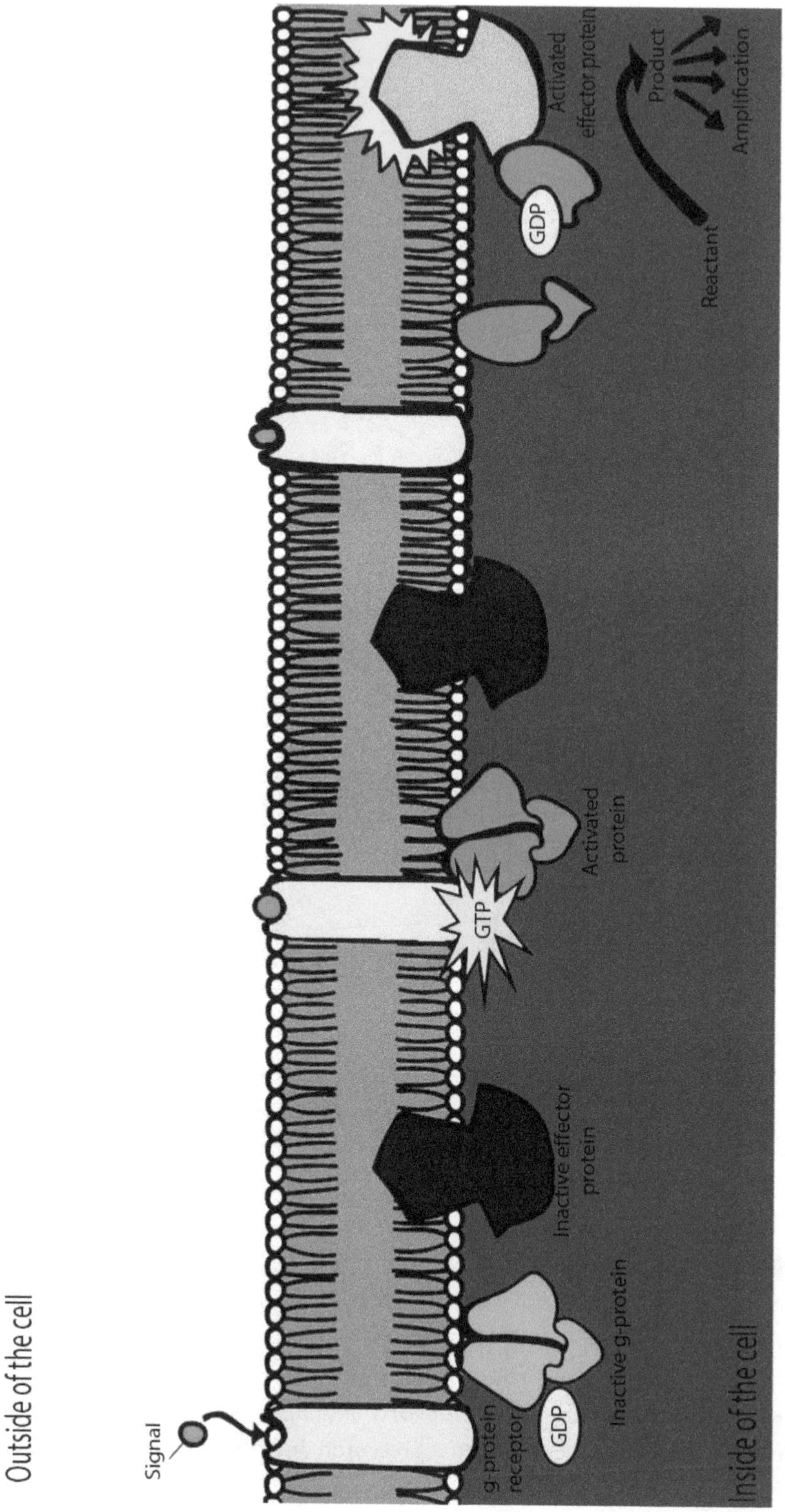

Figure 7.2 G-Protein Receptor

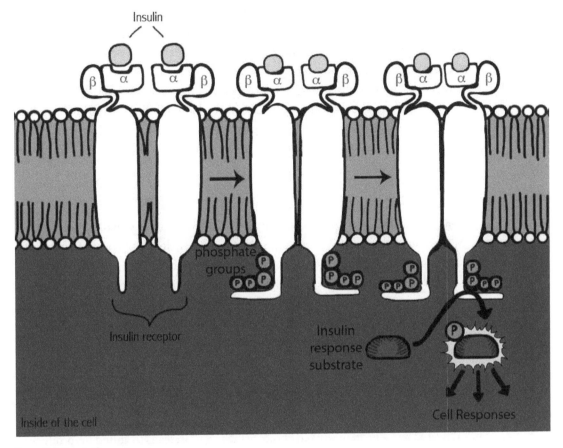

Figure 7.3 Protein Kinase Receptor

   **d. Protein kinase receptors** use second messengers. (See Figure 7.3)
      i.  These receptors speed up the addition of a phosphate group to another protein or themselves (we call this catalyzing **phosphorylation**), consequently activating them so they can work.
      ii.  One protein kinase activates the next, which activates the next, etc. We call this a **protein kinase cascade**.
  5.  Protein kinase cascade
    a.  A series of activated protein kinases leads to **signal amplification**, where each successive kinase activates even more kinases, amplifying the original signal.
      i.  Like a zombie apocalypse: One zombie quickly turns to three zombies, then each makes three more! One original zombie, now there are many.

b. The hormone **epinephrine** is involved in a cascade.

   i. Epinephrine, also known as adrenaline, is used in EpiPens to treat severe allergic reactions, or you may know it as the "rush" before you do something crazy; e.g., cliff diving.

   ii. Epinephrine is a great example of signal amplification because a single molecule of epinephrine translates to 10,000 molecules of blood glucose.

c. Different proteins at each step in the protein kinase cascade provide variation in the response, and sometimes this can go wrong.

   i. **Ras** is a protein that when activated causes cell division. However, if the signal accidently keeps getting sent and ras is continually activated by GTP, cell division keeps happening, allowing for tumor growth and potentially cancer.

## Section 7.2: Second messengers: What do they do, and what are the different types?

1. A second messenger's purpose is to amplify and distribute a cell's signal.

   a. Second messengers are like learning assistants. They help get the professor's message (signal) across to the students (other cells in the body).

      i. If they do well, students pass their tests (they got the message/signal).

   b. They activate many enzyme targets to carry out said signal.

   c. Sometimes involved in **crosstalk**

      i. Crosstalk is like listening to two conversations at the same time.

      ii. A signal might activate several different reactions or signal some and suppress others.

2. **cAMP** (cyclic AMP) is an example of a second messenger.

   a. Produced from ATP by the enzyme **adenylyl cyclase**

   b. Activated by a g protein–linked epinephrine receptor; leads to abundant production of cAMP

3. Most second messengers are formed when phospholipids in the plasma membrane are hydrolyzed by phospholipase.

   a. Ex.: Hydrolysis of $PIP_2$ to $IP_3$ + DAG → activated PKC → cell responses

   b. Know the above pathway, further explained here

      i. $PIP_2$ is hydrolyzed by **Phospholipase C** into $IP_3$ **and DAG**. Next $IP_3$ and DAG activate **protein kinase C (PKC)**. PKC can phosphorylate many proteins, leading to many cell responses.

   c. More specifically, $IP_3$ can open **calcium ($Ca^{2+}$)** channels, causing the concentration of $Ca^{2+}$ to increase in cytoplasm.

      i. $Ca^{2+}$ is a second messenger, which activates protein kinase C, controls channels, and stimulates secretion by exocytosis.

      d. Overactive $IP_3$/DAG leads to excessive brain activity in bipolar disorders.

          i. Lithium ions can help because they inhibit g protein activation of phospholipase C and synthesis of $IP_3$.

4. **Nitric oxide (NO)** gas: plays a role in acetylcholine and the relaxation of muscle

    a. Know this pathway

        i. Acetylcholine $\rightarrow IP_3 \rightarrow Ca^{2+} \rightarrow$ NO $\rightarrow$ cGMP $\rightarrow$ muscle relaxation

            1. **Acetylcholine** binds and activates receptor, producing $IP_3$.

            2. $IP_3$ opens up $Ca^{2+}$ channels, which causes synthesis of NO.

            3. NO acts as a second messenger because it allows cGMP to be created, leading to muscle relaxation.

    b. Key takeaways

        i. Concentration of NO is regulated by the amount of NO produced.

        ii. Concentration of $Ca^{2+}$ is regulated by membrane pumps and ion channels.

## Section 7.3: What happens after the signal pathway?

1. **Responses** to signals happen after pathways.

    a. Responses vary; could be cell division, ion channel opening, etc. A few examples are below.

    b. Smell from the opening of ion channels = neuron excitement.

        i. Results from the conformational change in a receptor (could be sound, taste, smell, doesn't have to be a ligand).

        ii. If you happen to not have a specific odor receptor, you won't be able to smell that specific scent. For example, if you can't smell eucalyptus, you don't have that odor receptor!

    c. Increase in enzyme activity: most common response

        i. Second messenger is phosphorylated by a receptor protein and then goes to activate an enzyme (causes a protein to change shape and reveal its activation site, or the receptor protein directly activates an enzyme), which activates another enzyme that can either inhibit or activate a reaction (an example of a cascade).

    d. Controls what proteins will be later synthesized (otherwise known as DNA transcription).

2. Communication between cells

    a. **Gap junctions**

        i. Allow direct connection and ability for cells to pass along molecules directly between cells, like ATP.

    b. Effective and efficient cell communication

    c. Hydrophilic channel

    d. Similar to **plasmodesmata** (the gap-like junctions in plants).

# CHAPTER SEVEN WORKSHEET ACTIVITIES

## Study Questions

1. What are the different secondary messengers, and in what pathways can you find them?
2. List and describe the four receptors mentioned in this chapter.
3. Explain the difference between direct and indirect signal transduction.
4. What is a protein kinase cascade, and how does it amplify a signal?

## Matching

1. ____Paracrine        A. Cell sends signals that affects itself
2. ____Autocrine        B. Cell sends signals to targets that are adjacent
3. ____Endocrine        C. Cell sends signals to cells nearby
4. ____Juxtacrine       D. Cell send signals to target cells far away

## Fill in the blanks

1. Ligands that are _____ bind to the extracellular portion of _____ _____, since these ligands are unable to cross the bilayer.
2. Protein kinases are a type of _____ that catalyzes the transfer of a _____ _____ from ATP to target molecule.
3. The binding of a phosphate group, known as _____, causes a change in charge, leading to an altered shape and function of the protein.
4. The _____ will bind instead of the ligand, preventing the signal from transmitting the information.
5. Cyclic AMP is a type of _____; these messengers serve to amplify and distribute the signal, activate enzymes, and are involved in crosstalk.

## Drawing activity

Use the whole paper and draw the different kinds of receptors: intracellular, g protein linked, protein kinase, and ion channel.

Intracellular

G protein

Protein Kinase

Ion Channel

# CHAPTER SEVEN PENCAST SUMMARY

Below is an outline of the pencast for Chapter 7. To review how to access this pencast, as well as pencasts for future chapters, please refer back to the introduction and read the instructions.

## Chapter Seven: Cell Communication and Multicellularity

**1:00–3:00: Cell membrane structure**
- Define *leukocyte*
- Endothelial EM
- Plasma membrane
- Inner life of the cell
- Cytoskeleton
  - Microfilaments
  - Actin filaments

**3:00–4:00: Cell movement**
- Inner cell
  - Microtubules
  - Microvilli
  - Motor proteins
  - Kinesin
  - Vesicles

**4:00–5:00: Cell organelles**
- Mitochondria
- Centrosome
- Endomembrane system
- mRNA translation

**5:10– 6:00: Protein synthesis**
- Ribosome protein synthesis in ER
  - Proteins leave the ER
  - Golgi
- Primary lysosome
- Secondary lysosomes

# 8

# ENERGETIC REACTIONS

## INTRODUCTION

When we think about cell (or human) movement, energy transformation, and metabolism, there's a lot that goes on along many intersecting biochemical pathways. You might have heard about one of these pathways, glycolysis, and how there are many components in a set order. Chemical reactions—including anabolic and catabolic reactions, kinetic and potential energy—are important attributes of metabolic and molecular change. When you think about energy transformations, consider the entire system where that energy is transformed. For a real-world perspective, a car engine can transfer energy to move the car, although not all the energy makes it to the wheels. Some energy is lost as heat; this lost energy isn't "**useful energy.**"

Math helps us understand "useful energy," and we can turn to $\Delta G$ (**free energy**) to explain energy in systems, including the chemical reactions that happen in these systems. The second law of thermodynamics supports the idea of **entropy**, which is the tendency of a system to become more disordered. This relates to spontaneous change. Think of an ice cube sitting on the counter. The ice cube has relatively low entropy because all of the water molecules are tightly bound [see Section 2.3]. However, at room temperature the ice begins to melt and becomes liquid water with molecules farther apart; this is an increase in entropy. This change from solid state water to liquid state water happens at a certain temperature. When you learn about disorder and energy transformations, whether exothermic or endothermic, it is very important to think about the $\Delta G$ (**free energy**), which is the energy used to do work; this is the energy coupled with the transformation we are explaining.

This chapter also introduces the role of **ATP**, which "powers" many **enzymes**. By lowering the **activation energy** of a reaction, these enzymes favor molecular change (they help reactions form products). Once you learn more about how enzymes function, ask yourself if you understand how ATP is used to energize a molecular change. Also think about how the size of the ΔG (and sign of the ΔG; negative is **exothermic** and positive is **endothermic**) explains how much useful energy is needed. To understand how enzymes speed up reactions, you will be introduced to enzyme kinetics and mechanisms. You will learn about **substrates** and how enzymes create a **transition state intermediate** that favors **product** formation by lowering the activation energy. Can you draw a graph that shows how enzymes lower energy barriers to create a greater amount of product?

There are several ways that enzymes catalyze the transformation of substrates into products. Enzymes can orient substrates, add chemical groups, and strain substrate bonds. Importantly, enzymes have extremely specific **active sites**, so they only operate on the substrates that fit into the active site. Be sure you can explain how enzymes are specific for only some substrates and how they catalyze reactions. In this chapter, you will also learn about **allostery**, which explains the mechanism for how enzymes can be regulated in a biochemical pathway. Therefore, reach for an emerging understanding of how different enzymes can act together in coordinated ways (how metabolic pathways intersect and how specific enzymes in these pathways can be controlled).

## TOPICS STUDENTS FOUND CHALLENGING

Students were surveyed just after they took an exam that emphasized the topics in this unit. The top areas these students found the most challenging are listed below.

- Difference between anabolic reactions vs. catabolic; exergonic vs. endergonic; ΔG (55%)
- Inhibitors (irreversible, reversible, competitive, uncompetitive, noncompetitive) (45%)
- Entropy vs. enthalpy (35%)
- Allosteric regulation (30%)

# CHAPTER EIGHT OUTLINE

## Section 8.1: What should you know about energy?

1.  There are many different forms of energy, yet it can be categorized into two major units.
    a.  **Potential**
        i.   Stored energy due to position
        ii.  Ex.: a roller coaster at the top of the incline
    b.  **Kinetic**
        i.   Energy of movement or work
        ii.  Ex.: a roller coaster moving up to the top then coming back down
2.  These two forms of energy are connected such that potential energy can change to kinetic energy and vice versa.
    a.  Ex.: A person sitting in a chair has energy stored in his or her muscles, potential energy, because the muscles are at rest. Once the person stands or begins to move, the muscles begin to do work, making motion, and that energy is now in use as kinetic energy.
3.  **Laws of thermodynamics:** These laws describe the changes in energy and how it relates to all organisms and matter.
    a.  First law
        i.   If two systems are independently in thermal equilibrium with a third system, they will be in equilibrium with one another.
    b.  Second law
        i.   Energy cannot be created or destroyed.
        ii.  Simply put, when converting energy, the total energy remains the same before and after.
    c.  Third law
        i.   Converting energy between forms loses some of that available energy, increasing the disorder in the system.
        ii.  **Entropy** is defined as the measure of disorder.
4.  **Total energy** in biological systems is the sum of usable and unusable energy.
    a.  Enthalpy (**H**): total energy.
    b.  Free energy (**G**): useable energy cells can use for biochemical reactions.
    c.  Entropy (**S**): unusable energy measured as disorder.
    d.  Temperature (T): absolute temperature.
5.  These quantities are related by:
    a.  $H = G + TS$
    b.  We are more focused on useable energy; therefore, we can rearrange the above formula to:

      i.   $G = H - TS$

  c. We are able to measure these variables at a constant temperature to identify the change ($\Delta$) occurring.

6. Free-energy change can be measured by the difference of energy in products and reactants.

  a. $\Delta G = G_{products} - G_{reactants}$

  b. These values can be positive or negative.

    i. Positive: Products have more free energy than the reactants → energy input (**endothermic**).

    ii. Negative: Products have less energy than reactants → energy output (**exothermic**).

  c. $\Delta G$ at a constant temperature is determined by the change in total energy and entropy.

    i.   $\Delta G = \Delta H - T\Delta S$

       1. In a chemical reaction:

         a. $-\Delta G$ → free energy released

         b. $+\Delta G$ → free energy used

         c. $+\Delta H$ → total energy added

         d. $-\Delta H$ → total energy released

         e. $\Delta S$ → sign and magnitude affects $T\Delta S$; may be large, small, positive, or negative.

  d. An increase in entropy for a chemical reaction shows that the products are more disordered.

  e. More products than reactants shows that it's free to move ($+\Delta S$).

  f. Fewer products than reactants shows that there is restriction in movement ($-\Delta S$).

## Section 8.2: What is the relationship between chemical reactions and energy?

1. Exergonic reactions

  a. Reactions that release free energy, $-\Delta G$

    i. Reactants → low energy products.

  b. Catabolic reactions cause disorder as they cause a breakdown.

  c. Think: The CAT always wrecks everything and destroys the room. (catabolism— breaking things down).

2. Endergonic reactions

  a. Reactions that need and use free energy, $+\Delta G$

    i. Reactants → high energy products.

  b. Anabolic reactions increase order as they form more complex structures.

3. Energy-coupling cycle

    a. Exergonic and endergonic reactions are coupled; is common in metabolism.
       i. Energy released from exergonic reactions is then used by endergonic reactions.
    b. ATP synthesis is an example of the energy-coupling cycle. If you understand the ADP →ATP→ ADP →ATP ... cycle, you understand the concept of energy coupling.

4. Chemical reactions are reversible.
    a. Concentration of the products and reactants will determine if the forward or reverse direction is favored.
    b. Chemical equilibrium: balance between the forward and reverse reaction.
       i. $\Delta G = 0$, state of no change

5. **Metabolism:** In biology we constantly refer to energy; more importantly, chemical energy. A major role of cellular metabolism is to create ATP. One of the most important topics is metabolism.

6. Metabolism is defined as the chemical reactions that occur in living organisms, allowing growth, reproduction, response to environments, and overall sustaining life.

7. Metabolism can be divided into two categories that are linked with one another: anabolism and catabolism.
    a. Anabolic reactions
       i. Require an input of energy to build things up
       ii. Ex.: linking amino acids to form proteins
    b. Catabolic reactions
       i. Breakdown of complex structures to their basic forms and release energy in the process
       ii. Ex.: breaking proteins down to their simple amino acids
    c. These two reactions are linked in the way that the energy released from degradation in catabolic reactions is then used in anabolic reactions for synthesis.

8. **ATP:** adenosine triphosphate (energy currency, nucleotide)
    a. Cells need ATP to capture and transfer energy in order to do work.
    b. Exergonic processes release energy → ADP takes that energy → converts to ATP.
       i. $ADP + P_i + \text{free energy} \rightarrow ATP + H_2O$
       ii. Formation of ATP is endergonic.
    c. Endergonic processes are driven by the free energy from the hydrolysis of ATP.
       i. $ATP + H_2O \rightarrow ADP + P_i + \text{free energy}$
       ii. Hydrolysis of ATP is exergonic, releases a large amount of free energy.
    d. The constant formation and hydrolysis of ATP → energy-coupling cycle → ATP is used and synthesized quickly.

## Section 8.3: What are enzymes, and how do they function?

1. **Enzymes** are proteins that act as biological catalysts to increase the rates of reactions.
   a. They DO NOT cause reactions, only speed up the rate at which the reaction occurs.
2. Enzymes are proteins named to reflect their function and usually will have the suffix *-ase*.
3. In order for reactions to occur, energy is needed.
   a. **Activation energy ($E_a$):** amount of energy needed to start a reaction
      i. Ex.: You are driving on the road (kinetic energy) and get stuck in a ditch (potential energy); to start moving you need a small amount of energy (activation energy) to push out of the ditch and continue moving.
      ii. Activation energy to start a reaction is recovered and is not part of $\Delta G$.
   b. Transition-state intermediate
      i. Unstable form of reactants in a chemical reaction caused by the activation energy
      ii. Higher free energy than the reactants and products.
   c. Enzymes are used to overcome energy barriers by lowering the activation energy needed to cause reactions.
      i. They DO NOT affect equilibrium.
4. Enzymes function with **specificity** for which reactants they bind and catalyze only a single reaction at a time.
   a. **Substrates** are the reactants in an enzymatic reaction that bind to the **active site** on an enzyme.
      i. Catalysis occurs at the active site of the enzyme.
   b. Enzyme-substrate complex: **E + S → ES → E + P**
      i. **ES** produced by the binding of a substrate to the active site and converts to the enzyme and product called an ES complex.
      ii. The enzyme (**E**) may change during the reaction, but it almost always reverts to its initial form and is ready for the next substrate.
      iii. Formation of the ES complex require less activation energy than the transition state intermediate, lowering the energy barrier, and speeds up the reaction in both directions.
      iv. Formation of the ES complex is reversible; therefore, ES can move forward to $E+P$, forming a product and regenerating the original enzyme. ES can also move in the reverse direction toward the reactants, forming the enzyme and substrate, E + S.
      v. It is important to remember that enzymes are NEVER consumed in chemical reactions.
      vi. This favors product formation because of the overall $\Delta G$ of the reaction.

c. The enzyme-catalyzed reaction reaches equilibrium faster than the uncatalyzed reaction.

    i. It DOES NOT change the concentration of the reactions or products. Final equilibrium is the same with or without the enzyme.

5. **Catalysis** mechanisms of enzymes

    a. **Acid-base:** Accelerating a chemical reaction by the addition of an acid or base, or both. The acid and/or base are not consumed in the reaction(s).

    b. **Covalent:** The enzyme contains a specific reactive group that attacks the substrate, resulting in accelerated hydrolysis that allows for covalent bonds between the residue and substrate.

    c. Metal ion: Allows for charge stabilization and shielding of negative charges and strategic positioning of $H_2O$.

6. Structure determines enzymatic functions.

    a. Enzymes pick the correct substrate based on how it locks with the active site.

        i. "Lock and key" refers to the idea of how a key is shaped precisely to fit a certain lock.

        ii. The enzyme's active site is the "lock," and only a specific substrate, "key," is shaped to fit the active site.

    b. Enzymes also can change their shape when binding to a substrate.

        i. **Induced fit:** change in shape to expose the active sites of the enzyme

7. Enzymes may need help to function.

    a. **Prosthetic groups:** organic or inorganic molecules that are tightly bound to proteins and involved in the active site of the enzyme to aid in its function

    b. **Cofactors:** inorganic compounds or metal ion(s) that loosely bind to "help" the enzyme during catalysis

    c. **Coenzymes:** organic molecules, such as vitamins, that loosely bind to allow the enzyme to be active

    d. Enzyme helper mnemonic: Everyone needs polite, cordial, company

        i. Enzymes—needs—prosthetic groups—cofactors—coenzymes

## Section 8.4: How are enzymes regulated?

1. **Metabolic pathways** show how the products of one reaction will act as the reactant in the next reaction.

    a. Activation or inactivation of enzymes determines the flow of these pathways.

2. Substrate concentration

    a. The rate of reaction increases as the substrate concentration increases, then it will level off (become **saturated**).

    b. At this point, the max rate has been reached; therefore, an increase in substrate concentration will not increase the reaction rate.

    i.   Saturation: All the enzymes are bound to substrates and working as fast as they can; the amount of product made will not increase with more substrates because there are no free enzymes to be used for catalysis.

3.   Regulation by **inhibitors**

   **a. Irreversible inhibition**

     i.   When certain side chains of the enzyme's active site are bound covalently by an inhibitor, it will cause permanent inactivation of the enzyme because it is unable to interact with its normal substrate.

   **b. Reversible inhibition**

     i.   Inhibitors noncovalently bind to the enzyme active site. These inhibitors are chemically similar to the substrate, so they can bind but will not allow the enzyme to function.

   **c. Competitive inhibitor:** Competes with substrate for enzyme's active site. Increasing the substrate concentration kicks the inhibitor from the active site, allowing the substrate to bind.

   **d. Noncompetitive inhibitor:** Binds to enzyme at a site different from the active site. It alters the enzyme function because the binding causes a change in shape, so the substrate may not be able to bind or will reduce product formation if it does bind.

   **e. Allosteric regulation**

     i.   **Effector molecule** binds to another site (not the active site) and causes the enzyme to change shape, which makes the substrate less attracted to the active site.

        1.   **Active form:** Enzyme shape fits substrate to bind; favors product formation.

        2.   **Inactive form:** Enzyme shape is unfit for substrate to bind.

**Study Tip 8.1:** Inhibitors can be tricky for students to remember; this can be helped with a bit of simple word association: Irreversible inhibition is changed chemically, so the enzyme activity is permanently affected. Reversible inhibitors have three classes: competitive, noncompetitive, and uncompetitive. Again, this is just a simple case of word association: Competitive has competition between the substrate and the inhibitor, in noncompetitive the inhibitor cheats and ruins the efficiency of the enzyme, and in uncompetitive the inhibitor waits for the enzyme and substrate to bond before joining. So: competitive = competition; noncompetitive = cheating; and uncompetitive = waiting.

4.   Effects of pH and temperature

   **a.** pH

i. Rate of reaction depends on the pH of the solution where the reaction is occurring. Each enzyme is active at a certain pH.

ii. If the pH increases or decreases more than optimally, the enzyme's activity will decrease.

iii. Substantial pH change will permanently deactivate the enzyme (proteolysis and/or **denaturation**).

b. **Temperature**

i. Increasing the temperature will increase the rate of reaction to a certain point.

ii. Many human enzymes are most active at 37°C. The enzyme Taq polymerase is most active from 75–80°C, since it is from a thermophilic (hot-loving) bacterium.

iii. Once temperatures become too high, they can cause an enzyme to be inactive because its structure changes and loses its function (denaturation).

## CHAPTER EIGHT WORKSHEET ACTIVITIES

### Short answer

1. State factors that affect enzyme activity and whether it is affected when increased or decreased.

2. Describe the following terms:
   a. activation energy
   b. allosteric regulation
   c. feedback inhibition
   d. competitive inhibitor
   e. noncompetitive inhibitor
   f. uncompetitive inhibitor

3. Describe entropy and explain how it is related to $\Delta G$.

4. List ways to regulate enzyme activity.

5. Define and list the function of:
   coenzyme
   cofactor
   prosthetic group

6. Define *bioluminescence*. List a few examples of organisms this is seen in.

## Fill in the blanks

1. When $\Delta G$ is negative, the reaction is _____, and when $\Delta G$ is positive, the reaction is _____.

2. Energy is released to cells in the form of _____ by the process of _____.

3. Enzymes aid in chemical reactions by _____ the activation energy.

4. The first law of thermodynamics states that energy _____ _____.

5. A substrate binds to an enzyme due to the _____ mechanism.

6. When a substrate binds to an enzyme, the shape of the enzyme is changed to create an _____.

7. Uncompetitive inhibitors bind to the _____.

8. Positive feedback is when a system tends to produce signals that will _____ the output.

9. The breakdown of ATP to yield energy is a(n) _____ reaction because the overall $\Delta G$ of the reaction is _____.

10. _____ are organic molecules that bind to the active site and have a critical role in enzyme activity.

11. Competitive inhibitors bind _____.

12. Noncompetitive inhibitors bind _____.

13. The formation of ATP is _____ where $\Delta G$ is _____. The breakdown of ATP is _____ where $\Delta G$ is _____.

14. _____ are organic or inorganic groups that permanently bind to enzymes to enhance its activity.

15. _____ are inorganic ions that bind to an enzyme to increase enzyme activity.

16. Zinc is an example of a(n) _____ that enhances enzyme activity.

17. _____ occurs when a molecule binds to a site other than the active site to induce a change to help control enzyme activity.

## Label the diagram

1.

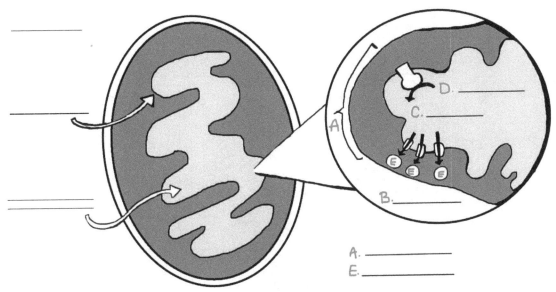

A. _____
E. _____

2.

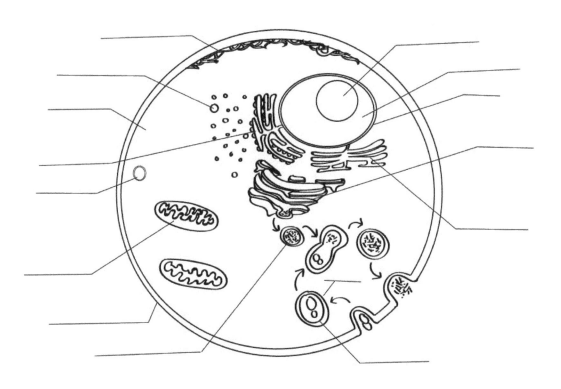

3.

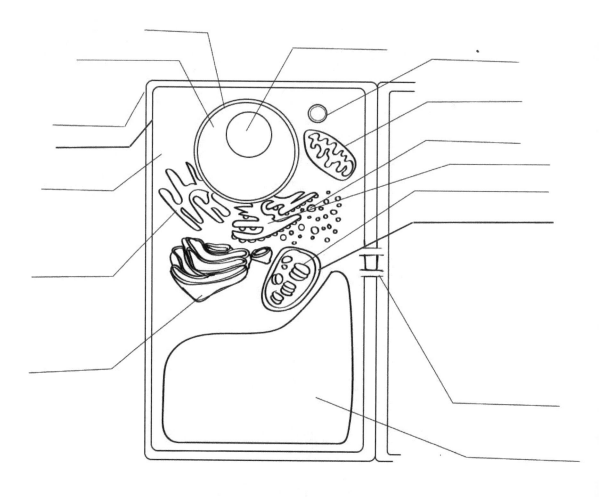

4.

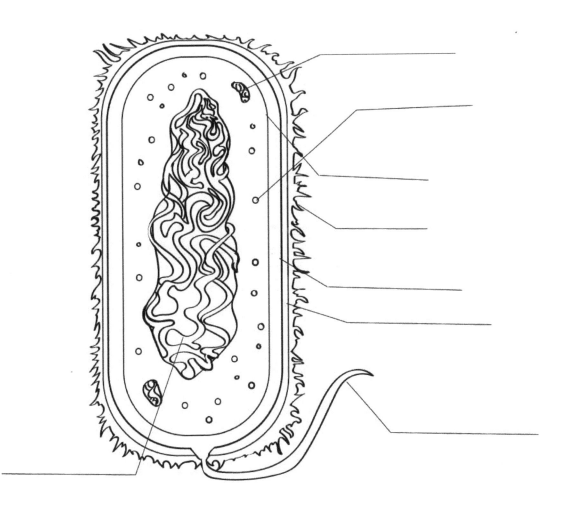

# CHAPTER EIGHT PENCAST SUMMARY

Below is an outline of the pencast for Chapter 8. To review how to access this pencast, as well as pencasts for future chapters, please refer back to the introduction and read the instructions.

## Chapter Eight: Energetic Reactions

0–4:00: Thermodynamics/free energy
- Law of thermodynamics
  - How organisms and cells transform energy to sustain life
    - Energy is neither created nor destroyed.
    - When energy is converted from one form to another, some of the energy becomes unusable to do work.
      - Entropy (S)
      - Temperature (T)
      - Free energy (G)
      - Enthalpy (H)
      - Δ: Change in variability quantity
    - $\Delta G = \Delta H - T \Delta S$

4:00–6:00: Exergonic and endergonic reactions
- Exergonic: energy released (catabolic)
  - Ex.: hydrolysis of ATP
- Endergonic: energy consumed (anabolic)
  - Ex.: synthesis of ATP, photosynthesis
- Equilibrium: Concentration of reactants and products have the tendency not to change.

6:00–8:00: Chemical equilibrium and reaction rate
- Without an enzyme, the reaction rate of substrate increases at slow linear rate.
- Enzyme catalyzed reaction, however, causes the reaction rate to increase exponentially.
- However, if there is a fixed amount of enzyme, and one just consistently adds substrates to it, the reaction rate still increases exponentially but will level off and reach equilibrium.
  - Maximum rate of reaction has been reached, because all enzyme active sites are occupied by a substrate.

# 9

# CELLULAR RESPIRATION

## INTRODUCTION

Students fear metabolism and photosynthesis more than other topics. In some ways it is important to think about respiratory metabolic pathways at the same time as photosynthesis because photosynthesis makes food for respiration. For this chapter we will focus on the metabolic pathways; the redox reactions we introduce will help us understand photosynthesis in the next chapter. These reactions allow for electron transfer to produce ATP using NADH and similar electron carriers. ATP can also be produced directly from enzymes by substrate-level phosphorylation. ATP production from enzymes does not produce nearly as much ATP as the electron transport chain, which is why electron transport is so important; it produces the bulk of ATP in the cell. This process happens in the cell membrane of prokaryotes and across the mitochondria of eukaryotes; in both cases this process is dependent on oxygen. If oxygen is not present, there is a bit of a dilemma: There is no ATP created because the electron carriers are not being cycled through the cell. Fermentation exists because of this problem. It is necessary to recycle the electron carriers when $O_2$ is absent. The two major types of fermentation to be aware of are lactic acid and alcoholic fermentation.

Redox reactions manage the gain and loss of electrons. These reactions can be confusing for students; however, they are crucial to understand how organisms obtain energy. Reactions that take place without oxygen are anaerobic, and reactions that use oxygen are aerobic. Think about Chapter 1, where we discussed life on Earth before photosynthesis and how eukaryotes are a product of aerobic reactions. Two main redox reactions to be aware of and understand are glucose oxidation and pyruvate oxidation. Think about how these processes begin and where they lead.

To cement your knowledge and understanding of cellular respiration, it is a good idea to examine the cell respiration pathways and their intermediate zones. In each pathway there are checkpoints that need to be met, where certain molecules such as carbon dioxide or acetyl-coA are produced and exchanged for hydrogen(s). Remember that transferring hydrogen ions goes hand in hand with transferring electrons; think about why this happens and its importance in cellular respiration.

**Study Tip 9.1:** Draw the electron transport chain and understand why hydrogen is being moved from the mitochondrial matrix into the intermembrane space.

**Study Tip 9.2:** Draw the mitochondria, be sure you can show where electron carriers are moving electrons between proteins and the respiratory chain. How does ATP synthase use $H^+$ to produce ATP? How many hydrogens are pumped across the membrane for each NADH or $FADH_2$ that enters electron transport, and how many ATPs are produced for each of those hydrogens? Look back on your drawing of the mitochondria when you explain. Your understanding of chemiosmotic theory and the mechanism of ATP synthesis will be a cornerstone of your understanding of metabolism. Ask yourself again what role oxygen and water play in this process. Then look at the fermentation pathways and consider why they are two different pathways.

**Study Tip 9.3:** Think about how electron carriers are chemically changed along these pathways. Consider your learning in Chapter 8 regarding regulation of metabolic pathways and see if you can make connections to some of the products of later pathways. For example, how is the rate of electron transport and ATP synthesis likely to influence the rate of metabolism in earlier pathways? How might fatty acid synthesis and degradation be relevant for regulating metabolic pathways that begin with glucose as a primary source of energy to produce ATP? How do we burn fat? How do we store fat? What molecules from this chapter could regulate this? By answering these questions, you will explain a major way that catabolism and anabolism are linked.

## TOPICS STUDENTS FOUND CHALLENGING

Students were surveyed just after they took an exam that emphasized the topics in this unit. The top areas these students found the most challenging are listed below.

- Electron carriers and their function (75%)
- Cellular respiration (70%)
- Glycolysis (65%)
- ATP conversion and net production of ATP (50%)
- Lactic acid fermentation (45%)

- Enzymes (45%)
- Citric acid cycle (35%)
- Chemiosmosis (30%)
- Oxidation/reduction (redox) reactions (30%)
- Hydrolysis (15%)

# CHAPTER NINE OUTLINE

## Section 9.1: What is oxidation reduction?

1. Oxidation-reduction reactions (redox reactions)
   a. Refers to three processes that harvest energy from glucose: glycolysis, cellular respiration, and fermentation.
2. Reducing agent vs. oxidizing agent. What is oxidation and reduction?
   a. **Oxidation** = loss of electrons
      i. Reducing agent = electron donor
   b. Reduction = gain of electrons
      i. Oxidizing agent = electron acceptor
   c. This can be confusing! Get them straight by writing it out. Notice that in REDuction you are REDucing the charge, because you are accepting an electron, which is negatively charged.
   d. OIL RIG: Oxidation is loss. Reduction is gain (of an electron).
3. How does this relate to hydrogen movement?
   a. When you transfer $H^+$ ions, you transfer electrons.
4. An example of a redox reaction is $NAD^+$ and NADH.
   a. $NAD^+$ is oxidized (loses an electron), and NADH is reduced (gains an electron)
   b. $NAD^+$ is a common **electron carrier**.
   c. NADH can be used to power later reactions that require energy.

## Section 9.2: What is a coenzyme?

1. It is a small molecule that assists in enzyme-catalyzed reactions (like metabolic pathways); an example is $NAD^+$.

## Section 9.3: What is glucose oxidation?

1. Glucose is broken down into six $CO_2$ and $H_2O$.
   a. What are oxidizing and reducing agents?
      i. Glucose is oxidized, so it is the reducing agent.

    ii.  Oxygen is the oxidizing agent; look at the electron transport chain and understand why.

  b. How are e-carriers involved?

    i.  Electron carriers are used for redox reactions. Think about concentration gradients, and look at your drawings to see where most electrons get transported.

  c. What are the other products of this process?

    i.  Ten NADH, two $FADH_2$, and four ATP.

2. Three separate stages of glucose oxidation: glycolysis, the citric acid cycle, and the <u>electron</u> transport chain.

## Section 9.4: Differences between aerobic and anaerobic reaction

1. **Aerobic** reactions happen in the presence of $O_2$.
2. **Anaerobic** reactions happen in the absence of $O_2$.
3. Under aerobic conditions: glycolysis → pyruvate oxidation → citric acid cycle/Krebs cycle → e⁻-transport + ATP synthesis.
4. Compare section 9.9, fermentation.

## Section 9.5: What is the output of glycolysis?

1. The process of converting one glucose molecule to two pyruvate molecules.
2. 1 glucose → 2 G3P → 2 pyruvate.
3. Glycolysis happens in the cytoplasm (outside mitochondria).
1. No photosynthesis to make glucose = no glucose for glycolysis = no energy.

## Section 9.6: What is pyruvate oxidation?

1. The process of oxidizing the two pyruvate molecules from glycolysis; yields acetate and $CO_2$.
2. **Pyruvate** is a three-carbon compound.
  a. Its major function is linking glycolysis to the citric acid cycle.
  b. Pyruvate is the end product from glycolysis. Pyruvate can be used in lactic acid fermentation as well as the citric acid cycle.
3. Energy from the process is captured by the reduction of $NAD^+$ to NADH, and the remaining energy is stored by binding acetate to coenzyme A (CoA), creating **acetyl CoA**.
  a. This happens in the mitochondrial matrix.
  b. Acetyl CoA is the first "ingredient" to the next step, citric acid cycle.
4. How many times does the glucose go through the citric acid cycle?

a. Twice; why?
   i.   Because you get two pyruvate molecules.
   ii.  So how many NADH do you get per glucose? Six.

## Section 9.7: What is the citric acid cycle (Krebs cycle)?

1. Takes acetyl-CoA produced from pyruvate oxidation, goes through the cycle twice; once per pyruvate.
2. The products you have from the one turn of Krebs cycle include:
   a. One $FADH_2$
   b. Two $CO_2$
   c. One ATP or GTP
   d. Three NADH
3. The direct production of ATP after completing both turns of the Krebs cycle is unimpressively two, but indirectly, a massive amount of ATP will be produced via $FADH_2$ and NADH reaching the electron transport chain.

## Section 9.8: What are oxidative phosphorylation, the electron-transport chain, and chemiosmosis?

1. How is oxidative phosphorylation different from substrate-level phosphorylation?
   a. Oxidative phosphorylation happens when an electron is donated from one molecule to another via the electron transport chain. Substrate-level phosphorylation is a direct process.
2. Refers to coupling of electron transport and ATP synthesis (chemiosmosis), since $H^+$ is concentrated to power ATP synthesis
3. Electron transport (See Figure 9.1)
   a. Moving electrons across the membrane makes energy, like moving water over a mill makes electricity/energy.
   b. Hydrogen ions are pumped against their concentration gradient, and the moving electron gradually loses energy. Oxygen accepts the electrons and reacts with $2H^+$ to form $H_2O$.
   c. Major function of mitochondria
   d. Be able to recognize the names of the enzymes involved, know how to group them, and be aware of the concentration gradient location of hydrogen ions in the mitochondria.
4. ATP synthesis, or **chemiosmosis**
   a. **ATP synthase** moves protons back across the inner membrane.
      i.   Creates a hydrogen ion (proton) channel/concentration gradient
      ii.  Makes A LOT of energy in the form of ATP

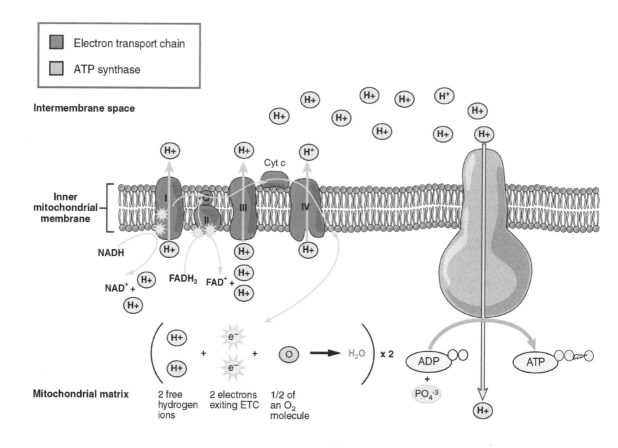

Figure 9.1 Electron Transport Chain Summary

1.  Passing a hydrogen ion through ATP synthase allows for a phosphate group to be added to ADP to create ATP.
b. Note: Hydrogen ions ($H^+$) are known as protons. The hydrogen ion has lost its only electron and is only a proton.
c. What function do hydrogen ion pumps serve? What is the end goal?
    i.  Hydrogen pumps are useful to move protons against their gradient into the inner membrane. This also allows for the regeneration of $NAD^+$ and $FAD^+$. Remember a product electron transport is water.

## Section 9.9: What is fermentation?

1.  The process of harvesting energy from glucose in anaerobic (without oxygen) conditions.
2.  Does not yield as much energy as the aerobic processes outlined above.

3. The two major kinds of fermentation are lactic acid fermentation and alcoholic fermentation.
   a. **Lactic acid fermentation:** Pyruvate is playing the role of the electron acceptor, and it occurs in microorganisms and some muscle cells. The product of this process is **lactic acid.**
   b. **Alcohol** fermentation: Occurs in yeast and plant cells. This process is used to produce alcoholic beverages. Products include **ethyl alcohol** and $CO_2$.

## CHAPTER NINE WORKSHEET ACTIVITIES

## Fill in the blanks

1. During fermentation, pyruvate is converted to either _____ or _____.
2. Reduction involves _____ of electrons, and oxidation involves _____ of electrons.
3. During metabolism, _____ and _____ are electron carriers involved in the redox process.
4. The citric acid (Krebs) cycle starts with the molecule _____.
5. During _____, ATP is generated from diffusion of _____ across mitochondrial membrane.
6. Glycolysis occurs in _____.
7. At the end of glycolysis, there are _____ net ATP generated.
8. When oxygen is absent, glycolysis proceeds to _____ process.
9. _____ is the process of ATP generation by the movement of protons across the mitochondrial membrane.
10. The end product of glycolysis is _____, which is oxidized to _____ and enters the citric acid cycle.
11. The electron transport chain occurs in the _____, where _____ occurs.
12. ADP is converted to ATP with the addition of Pi by the process called _____.
13. Glycolysis utilizes _____ glucose molecule(s).
14. The end product of the citric acid cycle is to produce _____ along with small amounts of GTP and reduced electron carrier molecules.
15. Most ATP is generated in the _____.
16. The _____ enzyme is essential for ATP synthesis by using an electro-chemical gradient.
17. The electron transport chain consists of _____ enzyme complexes.

18. The purpose of pumping H⁺ ions across mitochondrial membrane is to create a
_____.

19. ATP synthase consists of two motor parts: _____ and _____.

20. ATP production has low yield due to impermeability of mitochondria to
_____.

## Label the following

22) The name of this is _____?

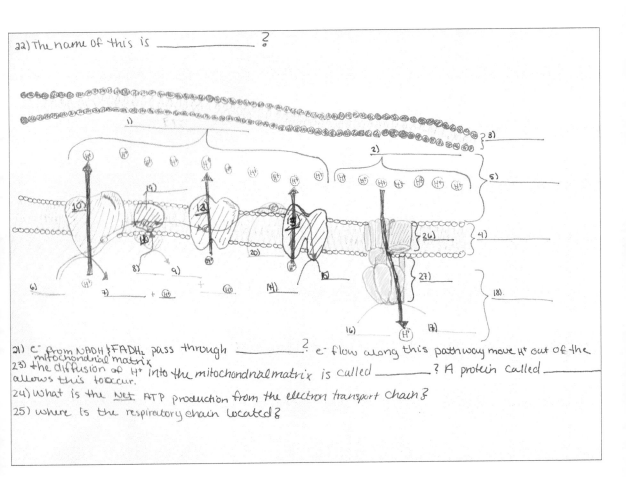

1)

2)

3)

4)

5)

6)

7)

8)

9)

10)

11)

12)

13)

14)

15)

16)

17)

18)

19)

20)

21) e⁻ from NADH & FADH₂ pass through _____? e⁻ flow along this pathway move H⁺ out of the mitochondrial matrix

23) the diffusion of H⁺ into the mitochondrial matrix is called _____? A protein called _____ allows this to occur.

24) What is the Net ATP production from the electron transport chain?

25) where is the respiratory chain located?

Glycolysis

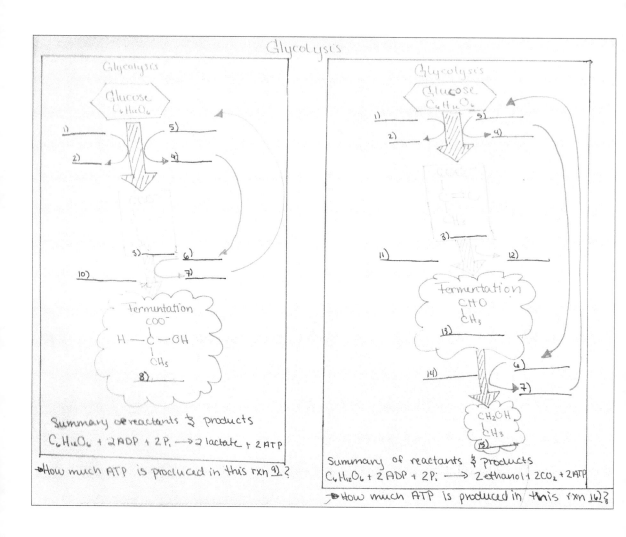

Summary of reactants & products

$C_6H_{12}O_6 + 2ADP + 2P_i \longrightarrow 2$ lactate $+ 2$ ATP

How much ATP is produced in this rxn 9) ?

Summary of reactants & products

$C_6H_{12}O_6 + 2ADP + 2P_i \longrightarrow 2$ ethanol $+ 2CO_2 + 2$ ATP

How much ATP is produced in this rxn 16) ?

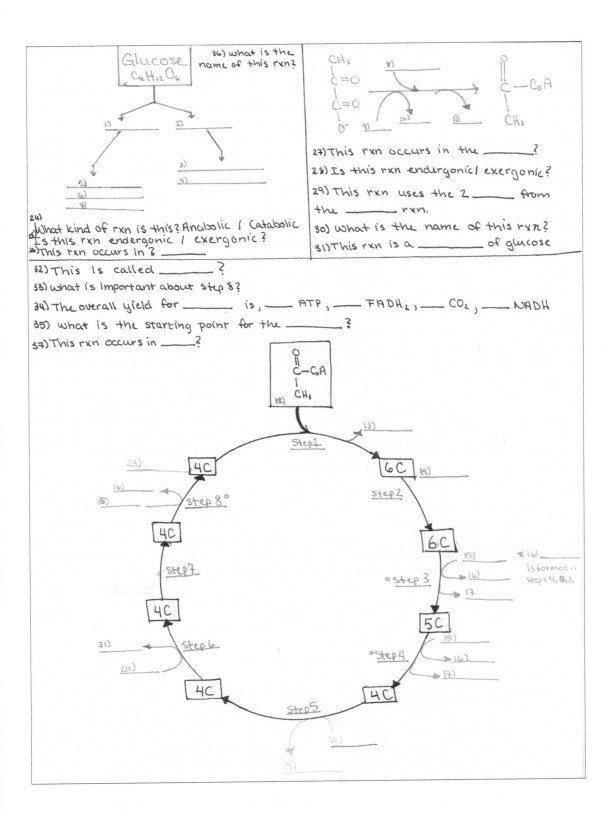

Glucose
$C_6H_{12}O_6$

36) what is the name of this rxn?

1) _____  2) _____

3) _____
4) _____

5) _____
6) _____
7) _____

24)
a) What kind of rxn is this? Anabolic / Catabolic
b) Is this rxn endergonic / exergonic?
26) This rxn occurs in? _____

$CH_3$
$|$
$C=O$
$|$
$C=O$
$|$
$O^-$   9)

8)

10)   11)

$C-CoA$
$||$
$O$
$CH_3$

27) This rxn occurs in the _____?
28) Is this rxn endergonic / exergonic?
29) This rxn uses the 2 _____ from the _____ rxn.
30) what is the name of this rxn?
31) This rxn is a _____ of glucose

32) This is called _____?
33) what is important about step 8?
34) The overall yield for _____ is, ___ ATP, ___ $FADH_2$, ___ $CO_2$, ___ NADH
35) what is the starting point for the _____?
37) This rxn occurs in _____?

$O$
$||$
$C-CoA$
$|$
12)   $CH_3$

13) _____

Step 1

4C   23) _____

6C   14) _____

16) _____
15) _____   Step 8°

Step 2

4C

6C

15) _____
16) _____
17

✱ 16) _____
is formed..
steps 4, 8, 3.

Step 7

° step 3

4C

5C

21) _____   Step 6

20) _____

15) _____
° step 4
16) _____
17) _____

4C

4C

Step 5

18) _____

19) _____

# CHAPTER NINE PENCASTS SUMMARY

Below is an outline of the pencast for Chapter 9. To review how to access this pencast, as well as pencasts for future chapters, please refer back to the introduction and read the instructions.

## Chapter Nine: Cellular Respiration

**0–2:30: What is cellular respiration?**
- ○ Cell respiration is exergonic.
- ○ Understand the equation for cell respiration.
- ○ Takes place inside mitochondria

**2:30–5:30: Glycolysis**
- ○ Takes place outside mitochondria in cytoplasm.
- ○ Aerobic and anaerobic pathways.
- ○ Produce two molecules of pyruvate.
- ○ Halfway through: pair of G3P molecules.
  - ○ They gain another phosphate group, causing it lose an H atom and two electrons → oxidize.
  - ○ Electrons added to NAD+ making NADH.
- ○ End result of glycolysis: 2 pyruvate, 2 ATP, and 2 NADH.
- ○ Pyruvate gets passed into mitochondria.
- ○ They are converted through oxidation and into an acetyl group (or acetate) and $CO_2$.

**5:30–7:30: Citric acid cycle**
- ○ Once acetyl + CoA is created, it can enter citric acid cycle.
- ○ Inside mitochondria matrix.
- ○ CoA breaks off acetate molecule (recycled to help create more acetyl CoA); what's left binds with oxaloacetate, which then forms citrate (also known as citric acid).
- ○ Citrate is oxidized, releases $CO_2$ and proton and 2 electrons, and joins NAD+ → NADH.
- ○ Another oxidation → releases $CO_2$ and another NAD+ → NADH.
- ○ Another oxidation → 2 hydrogen and 2 electrons and FADH is reduced → $FADH_2$

**7:30–10:30: Electron transport chain**
- ○ NADH and $FADH_2$ (which carries electrons, aka energy) move through a

series of proteins.

- o Electrons are transported to next protein.
- o Protons (hydrogen ions) are pumped out through each protein in the inner membrane space of the mitochondria.
- o Proton concentration increases, causing matrix to be charged, creating a gradient.
- o These $H^+$ go through the ATP synthase, powering it.
    - o ATP uses the potential energy created from the gradient to turn ADP into ATP; called chemiosmosis.
- o Oxygen is the final electron acceptor; accepts electrons and binds with hydrogen to create water.
- o Products of electron transport chain: water and ATP (36).

# PHOTOSYNTHESIS

## INTRODUCTION

Photosynthesis is the process when plants and other organisms use water, carbon dioxide ($CO_2$), and sunlight to make oxygen ($O_2$) and sugar ($C_6H_{12}O_6$). Our world as we know it would not be the same without this process! Photosynthesis is a redox reaction [see Section 9.1] where water is oxidized to form $O_2$, and $CO_2$ is "fixed" in later metabolic steps to become larger carbohydrates. It is important to know what role water plays in photosynthesis.

There are two pathways for photosynthesis that occur in the chloroplasts; light-dependent reactions and light-independent reactions. Light energy is converted to chemical energy during the **light-dependent reactions,** and the chemical energy is used to reduce $CO_2$ to carbohydrates in the **light-independent reactions**.

Cyclic and noncyclic electron transport (parts of the light-dependent reactions) can be particularly confusing for students to follow. Key things to remember are that noncyclic electron transport uses both photosystem I and II to produce NADPH, ATP, and $O_2$, while the cyclic electron transport only uses photosystem I and only produces ATP.

**Study Tip 10.1:** It is recommended for students to draw the Z scheme model for noncyclic electron transport, paying close attention to the order of the photosystems and what molecules are formed during each stage.

The **Calvin cycle** is the main part of the light-independent reactions. While the cycle does not utilize light energy directly, it does use the NADPH and ATP generated in the light-dependent reactions to reduce $CO_2$ in the stroma to a carbohydrate. There are three processes of the Calvin cycle we will learn about: fixation, reduction, and regeneration. Students need to know the products of those processes and how photorespiration recovers some of the carbon that is channeled away from the Calvin cycle. Six turns of the cycle produce one molecule of glucose, although usually three

carbon sugars are more useful to a plant. This chapter is full of chemistry details and has many moving parts. Take your time.

## TOPICS STUDENTS FOUND CHALLENGING

Students were surveyed just after they took an exam that emphasized the topics in this unit. The top areas these students found the most challenging are listed below.

- CAM plants (90%)
- Enzyme RuBisCO and its function (Calvin cycle) (80%)
- Difference between photosynthesis I and II (50%)
- Photophosphorylation (45%)

## CHAPTER TEN OUTLINE

### Section 10.1: What is photosynthesis?

1. Sunlight is used to synthesize food (glucose) and oxygen using carbon dioxide and water.
    a. $6CO_2 + 6H_2O \rightarrow C_6H_{12}O_6 + 6O_2 + 6H_2O$
        i. Autotrophs are organisms that produce food.
        ii. Heterotrophs are organisms that cannot produce food, and thus they consume other organisms.
    b. Since photosynthesis releases oxygen, the efficiency rate of photosynthesis is measured by the amount of oxygen released in the environment.
    c. Stable $^{18}O$ radioactive isotopes were used to determine that water is the source of $O_2$.
    d. Photosynthesis is a redox reaction where water is oxidized and carbon dioxide is reduced.
2. Chloroplasts are plastids where photosynthesis occurs.
    a. Stacks of thylakoids form grana.
    b. Stacks of grana are found within the chloroplast.
    c. Light-independent reactions happen in the stroma—the space outside the grana.

## Section 10.2: Light and pigment

1.  Light is electromagnetic radiation made of photons, which are particles that travel in waves.
    a.  The amount of energy is inversely proportional to its wavelength.
2.  When a photon hits a molecule, one of the following can happen:
    a.  Bounce off
    b.  Pass through
    c.  Be absorbed
        i.  Electrons in a molecule are in **a ground state** when it is not hit by a photon.
        ii. When absorbed by a molecule, a photon adds energy to the molecule, making the molecule excited and unstable.
        iii. Ground state electrons enter an excited state. These electrons can transfer their energy to other molecules.
3.  Pigments are molecules that absorb light.
    a.  The most important pigment in photosynthesis is chlorophyll a, which absorbs red and blue colors and scatters green. The reason plants are green is because we see the green wavelength chlorophyll reflects. It has a hydrocarbon tail that anchors it into a protein in a thylakoid photosystem.
4.  Absorption spectrum is a plot showing the absorption of wavelengths by a pigment. This energy is mostly used in photosynthesis.
5.  Action spectrum is a plot of photosynthesis against wavelengths of light.
6.  Accessory pigments are located around the reaction center and consist of chlorophyll b, chlorophyll c, and carotenoids.

## Section 10.3: What are light-dependent reactions?

1.  Photosystems are protein complexes where the conversion of light energy to chemical energy takes place.
    a.  They are made of a protein complex that captures the light energy within a **reaction center**.
    b.  An electron (from the water molecule) absorbs the energy and becomes excited (photoexcitation).
    c.  The excited chlorophyll gives away an electron to an acceptor.
2.  Photosynthesis II (See Figure 10.1)
    a.  **Occurs before photosynthesis I**; chlorophyll absorbs at 680 nm.
    b.  A photon hits a reaction center that contains $P_{680}$.
    c.  When excited, electrons move from one energy state to another (electron transport chain).

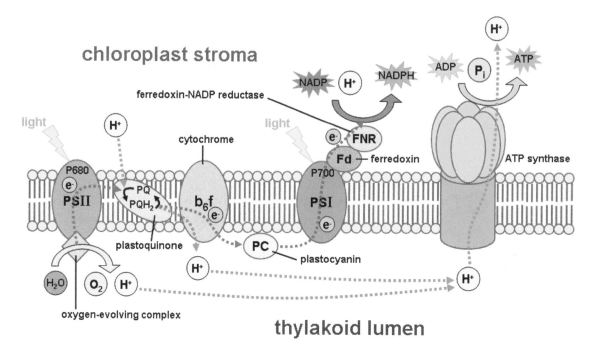

chloroplast stroma

thylakoid lumen

Figure 10.1 Electron Transport Chain Summary

*SOURCE: Tameeria, "Thylakoid membrane," https://commons.wikimedia.org/wiki/File:Thylakoid_membrane.png. Copyright in the Public Domain.*

    d. Electrons are transported from one carrier to another. Energy states get lower as the electron travels from one protein to another. The energy has been used to pump $H^+$ into the thylakoid lumen, creating a proton gradient used to produce ATP by ATP synthase (photosynthesis I).

3. Photosynthesis I
    a. **Occurs after photosynthesis II**; chlorophyll absorbs at 700 nm.
    b. Photons are absorbed by the reaction center that contains $P_{700}$.
    c. The electron transported by photosynthesis II is received by the reaction center containing $P_{700}$ and is further excited by photons here.
    d. $NADP^+$ reductase needs two $H^+$ in order to produce NADPH. A second electron is transported from photosynthesis II.
    e. Generation of NADPH and ATP will be used in the light-independent reactions.

## Section 10.4: What are light-independent reactions?

1. Light-independent reactions/Calvin cycle (See Figure 10.2)
    a. Not dependent on light, but dependent on the products produced in light-dependent reactions (ATP and NADPH).
    b. $CO_2$ reaches the mesophyll cells through stromata, where it reaches chloroplast in many C3 plants.

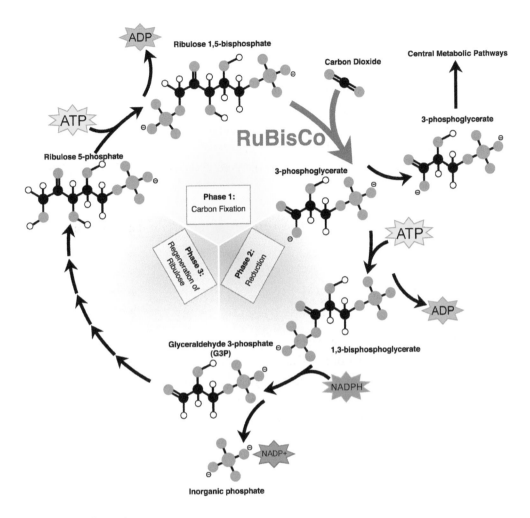

Figure 10.2 Calvin Cycle
*SOURCE: Copyright © Yikrazuul (CC BY-SA 3.0) at https://commons.wikimedia.org/wiki/File:Calvin_cycle.svg.*

2. First step of **Calvin cycle:** fixation of $CO_2$
    a. The stage where carbon is fixed into organic molecules.
    b. Three main components of $CO_2$ fixation are: $CO_2$, **RuBisCO** (enzyme), and three molecules of RuBP carboxylalse (five carbon atoms and two phosphates).
    c. One molecule of $CO_2$ reacts with one molecule of RuBP, producing two molecules of **3PG** (or PGA, depending on which textbook you have) per cycle. RubisCO catalyzes the reaction.
    d. While the number of carbon atoms remains the same, carbon dioxide is transformed into an organic compound.
3. Second step of Calvin cycle: reduction
    a. Transformation of six molecules of 3PG into six molecules of G3P using six molecules of ATP and NADPH (reduction reaction).

    **b.** ATP is transformed into ADP (loss of phosphate group), while NADPH is transformed into $NADP^+$ (loss of $H^+$).

4. Third step of Calvin cycle: regeneration
    **a.** Three molecules of ATP are used in this stage.
    **b.** The Calvin cycle has to cycle three times to fix enough carbon for one molecule of G3P to be transported out of the cycle.
    **c.** While one G3P molecule is sent to the cytoplasm, the other five G3Ps left are used to regenerate RuBP.

**Study Tip 10.2:** Make a chart to differentiate between the light-dependent and light-independent reactions.

## Section 10.5: C3, C4, and CAM plants

1. C3 plants
    **a.** Photosynthesis occurs in the mesophyll.
    **b.** Make up the majority of the plants.
    **c.** The reaction happens in the mesophyll cell. Carbon dioxide is converted into 3PG catalyzed by RuBisCO to produce glucose.
    **d.** On hot days the stomata close to prevent water loss. $CO_2$ is not able to enter once the stomata close and photorespiration occurs.
    **e.** Advantage in cold weather.
    **f.** Ex.: wheat and rice.

2. C4 plants
    **a.** Photosynthesis occurs in mesophyll cells and in bundle sheath cells.
    **b.** **Oxaloacetate** is the first product.
    **c.** In the mesophyll cell, $CO_2$ is fixed into **PEP**, by **PEP carboxylase**, and then to oxaloacetate.
    **d.** Malate is produced from oxaloacetate in bundle sheath cells, which is decarboxylated to pyruvate and $CO_2$.
    **e.** While pyruvate returns to mesophyll cells to produce ATP, $CO_2$ initiates the Calvin cycle.
    **f.** Advantage in hot weather.

3. CAM (crassulacean metabolism) plants.
    **a.** Photosynthesis occurs in mesophyll cells with large vacuoles.
    **b.** Fixed into a 4-C molecule by PEP carboxylase.
    **c.** Night: $CO_2$ is fixed by PEP carboxylase, stomata are open, and malate is stored.
    **d.** Day: malate is decarboxylated, and stomata are closed.
    **e.** Ex.: succulents, cacti, pineapples.

# CHAPTER TEN WORKSHEET ACTIVITIES

## Short answer

1. Write down the complete balanced reaction for photosynthesis. State what is reduced and oxidized from the reactants.
2. Explain the two different types of electron transport systems in mitochondria and chloroplasts.
3. What does it mean for a plant to be photoautotrophic—what is the significance of this?
4. List the primary $CO_2$ acceptors, as well as the $CO_2$ fixing enzyme in C3, C4, and CAM plants.

## Fill in the blanks

1. Photosynthesis is the process of utilizing light energy from the sun to convert _____ and _____ to _____ and _____.
2. A stack of thylakoids is called _____.
3. Exchange of gases ($CO_2$ and $H_2O$) occurs through a pore called _____.
4. Water uptake from roots occurs through _____.
5. The Calvin cycle occurs in the _____ of the chloroplast.
6. The light-dependent stage occurs in the _____.
7. In the light-dependent stage, electrons are transferred from _____ to _____ via the _____.
8. The end product of the light-dependent stage is _____ and _____.
9. _____ is the last electron carrier that is responsible for production of NADPH.
10. Photolysis of _____ occurs to produce oxygen, $H^+$ ions, and $2e^-$.
11. The gain of electron is _____, whereas the loss of electron is _____.
12. The light-independent reactions are also known as the _____.
13. _____ is the enzyme essential for carbon fixation in the Calvin cycle.
14. The Calvin cycle has to run _____ times to produce one molecule of glucose.
15. Photorespiration is observed in _____ plants.

## Draw and label the following

Your drawings of the chloroplast will be an anchor for you to explain photosynthesis and conceptually understand the production of ATP and NADPH in a cycle between the light-dependent reactions and the light-independent reactions. Draw the structure of a chloroplast and be sure to include these features:

1. Thylakoid
2. Granum
3. Stroma
4. Lumen
5. Inner and outer membrane of chloroplast
6. Lamella

# CHAPTER TEN PENCAST SUMMARY

Below is an outline of the pencast for Chapter 10. To review how to access this pencast, as well as pencasts for future chapters, please refer back to the introduction and read the instructions.

## Chapter Ten: Photosynthesis

1:30–2:30: **Anatomy of the chloroplast**
- o  Take a look at the structure of chloroplast and make sure to know all the organelles necessary for photosynthesis: thylakoid (light reactions), grana, stroma (light independent reactions).
- o  Know the equation of photosynthesis: $6H_2O + 6CO_2$ + light (energy) = $C_6H_{12}O_6$ (glucose) + $6O_2$ (opposite of cellular respiration).
- o  Photosynthesis is an endergonic reaction (opposite of cellular respiration).

2:30–7:30 **Light-dependent reactions (electron transport chain)**
- o  Use light energy to drive the reaction.
- o  Chlorophyll is the necessary pigment to absorb the photons; two types: a and b.
- o  Step 1: Photon hits chlorophyll (electron).
- o  Step 2: The electron becomes unstable and jumps up an energy level.
- o  Step 3: Electron gets transferred into an electron acceptor.
- o  Step 4: Electron moves from one acceptor to another, producing chemical energy (ATP).
- o  Step 5: Electron transport chain: noncyclic—uses two photosynthesis: II and I, aka Z scheme.
- o  Step 6: Photosynthesis II: splitting of $H_2O$ -> $2e + 1/2O_2 + 2H_2$
- o  Step 7: Photosynthesis I: $2e$ + NADP+ $H^+$ -> NADPH

7:30–9:30 **Light-independent reactions (Calvin cycle—carbon fixation)**
- o  Uses NADPH and ATP instead of the light energy
- o  Step 1: 6 Carbon molecule breaks into 2 3PG (RuBisCO enzyme).
- o  ADP and NADP+ are produced.
- o  Step 2: Two G3P molecules are produced (the other 10 get recycled).
- o  Step 3: Through ATP phosphorylation they become RuBP, which starts the Calvin cycle.
- o  Six cycles of Calvin cycle to produce one molecule of glucose

10:00–12:30: **Photorespiration**
- o $O_2$ consumed, $CO_2$ released
- o CAM plants (pineapple, cacti)
- o Take in $CO_2$ at night and store it in malic acid
- o $CO_2$ in malic acid used in daytime
- o C4 plants (corn, sugarcane)
- o Synthesize oxaloacetate
- o Oxaloacetate converted to malate
- o Malate releases $CO_2$ into bundle sheath cells.

# CELL DIVISION
## MEIOSIS AND MITOSIS

### INTRODUCTION

Cell division is one of the most important processes that happen for anything that is living. Importantly, cell division is different for eukaryotes and prokaryotes, and eukaryotic cells have both mitosis and meiosis (meiosis I and meiosis II). For a cell to divide, it must first receive a reproductive signal; cyclin-dependent kinase (CDK) enzymes highly regulate cell division and help control the cell cycle. The DNA in any cell must be replicated and separated. In prokaryotic cells this process of cell division is simple, because there is only one chromosome. Prokaryotes divide by **binary fission**. The chromosome is replicated, and the copies are attached to different parts of the cell membrane; these areas will then separate and become new cells. In a eukaryotic cell the process of division is not as simple, because the cell has more chromosomes and is more complex. When somatic cells—the cells that make up most of our organs and body parts—divide, the process is called mitosis. Mitosis forms two genetically identical diploid (2n) daughter cells. Sex cells (gametes), on the other hand, are divided through a process called meiosis, which produces four haploid (n) daughter cells that are genetically different from the parent cell (2n).

The overall process of cell division can be broken down into three parts: interphase, signal reception, and mitosis. Interphase is the longest part of the cycle and is composed of three subphases: G1, S, and G2. G1 has the longest duration and is considered the growth phase. S is when the DNA is replicated, and G2 is when the cell prepares itself to divide, but no actual division has happened. During each of these phases, a signal involving CDK permits the cell cycle to continue without error. The process of mitosis is relatively short and can be remembered using this anagram: PPMAT. The phases of mitosis are responsible for creating two identical daughter cells; these phases can be distinguished using a light microscope.

To understand the differences between mitosis and meiosis, it is valuable to distinguish the end products. Note the differences between the meiosis I and meiosis II chromosomes. It will also be beneficial to understand how errors during meiosis can complicate life. Fortunately, meiosis gives life incredible genetic diversity.

At this time it is also important to understand cell death. The two different types are necrosis and apoptosis. Necrosis is typically an involuntary cell death that can negatively affect surrounding cells, while apoptosis is programmed cell death that does not cause as much damage. Understanding cell death, and its importance, will be useful when learning about tumors and metastasis.

## TOPICS STUDENTS FOUND CHALLENGING

Students were surveyed just after they took an exam that emphasized the topics in this unit. The top areas these students found the most challenging are listed below.

- Differentiation between meiosis and mitosis (90%)
- The Ras pathway in cancer cells to understand metastasis (45%)

## CHAPTER ELEVEN OUTLINE

### Section 11.1: Cell division in prokaryotes vs. eukaryotes

1. Cell division basics: Four events must occur for cell division.
   a. Reproductive signal
   b. Replication of DNA
   c. Segregation or the separation of replicated DNA into two **daughter cells**
   d. **Cytokinesis**, the act of the cells separating and forming two new cells.
2. Prokaryotic vs. eukaryotic cell division
   a. Binary fission is when a prokaryotic cell replicates its strand of DNA and then splits into two new cells.
      i. This is NOT the same thing as mitosis!
   b. Prokaryotes have one chromosome and form a circle.
   c. It is uncommon to see a prokaryote divide by anything other than binary fission.
   d. The two important regions of bacterial chromosomes to know are:
      i. *Ori-* or "origin" site where replication begins.
      ii. *Ter-* where the replication is terminated.

Figure 11.1 Mitosis in Eukaryotic Cells

*SOURCE: LadyOfHats, "Mitosis division in Eukaryotic cells," https://commons.wikimedia.org/wiki/File:Mitosis_cells_se-quence.svg. Copyright in the Public Domain.*

3. **Cytokinesis** is when a plasma ring starts closing in between the two new cells, pinching them off.
   a. New parts to the membrane are synthesized to fully encapsulate each cell individually.
4. Eukaryotes have a more complex way of dividing and making daughter cells, in part because eukaryotes have more chromosomes.
   a. **Mitosis:** forms two genetically identical diploid (2n) daughter cells (See Figure 11.1)
      i. Common for cells that make up most of our organs and skin, called "somatic" cells.
   b. **Meiosis:** forms four genetically different haploid (n) daughter cells (See Figure 11.2)
      i. We see this in gametes, or sex cells (egg and sperm).
      ii. Our gametes are haploid (n) because two of them will fuse together to form a diploid (2n) zygote.

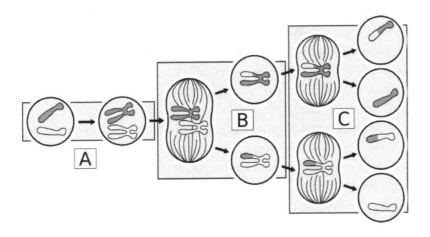

Figure 11.2 Major Events in Meiosis

*SOURCE: ParticiaR, "Major Events in Meiosis," https://commons.wikimedia.org/wiki/File:MajorEventsInMeiosis_variant_int.svg. Copyright in the Public Domain.*

## Section 11.2: The cell cycle

1. The overall cycle consists of three large periods.
   a. **Interphase:** When the nucleus is visible and the DNA is unwound inside. Also consists of three subphases.
      i. **G1:** Chromosomes are single and unreplicated, and this phase can last from minutes to years.
         1. This is considered a growth phase. The cell will not divide unless it is of an adequate size.
      ii. **S phase:** The DNA starts to replicate, and sister chromatids become visible.
      iii. **G2:** The microtubules and filaments used to move the sister chromatids begin to form, and the cell is preparing to divide.
         1. Note: The cell has not divided, and chromosomes have not moved anywhere yet!
2. The way cells know when to continue through the different subphases is when they receive a signal from a **cyclin-dependent kinase** (CDK).
   a. Cyclin activates CDK by binding to the cyclin.
   b. If the cell reaches the **checkpoint** at the end of its subphase but is not ready to divide, the CDK will not allow the cell to continue until it is 100% ready.
      i. Checkpoints exist near the end of G1 and G2/mitosis transition.
      ii. DNA damage is a major reason the cell cycle would not proceed.
3. Mitosis
   a. In mitosis, two identical daughter cells are formed.
4. The phases of mitosis
   a. **Prophase: Chromatin** begins to condense and wraps itself around proteins called histones to help with coiling.
   b. **Prometaphase:** The nuclear envelope begins to disintegrate, and the **spindle fibers** that were forming in G2 now connect to the chromosomes.
   c. **Metaphase:** All chromosomes are attached to spindles and are aligned with their homologous pair at the midline of the cell.
   d. **Anaphase:** The spindles start to pull at the chromosomes, moving them to opposite sides of the cell.
      i. Chromatids are now called **daughter chromosomes** with their own **centromere** (point where a spindle fiber attaches).
      ii. Note how the chromosomes move; the spindle fibers reel them toward their proper poles.
   e. **Telophase:** The nuclear envelope forms around the two new sets of chromosomes at opposite poles, and the chromosomes begin to uncoil.
5. The **spindle apparatus** is an important set of microtubules that pull the sister chromatids apart.
   a. Emanate from an organelle called the centrosome, containing two **centrioles.**

    b. Two main types of microtubules in the spindles

        i. Polar microtubules.

        ii. Kinetochore microtubules.

6. Each **chromatid** has a **kinetochore**.

    a. The **kinetochore** is the site where the microtubules attach to the chromatids.

7. **Cytokinesis** is when the cytoplasm begins to divide.

    a. Microfilament ring squeezes off the two cells.

        i. This ring is composed of myosin and actin.

## Section 11.3: Meiosis and mitosis

1. **Meiosis** has two nuclear divisions.

    a. DNA only replicated once.

    b. Makes haploid (n) gametes (sex cells).

2. Meiosis I

    a. **Prophase I:** Homologous chromosomes pair with each other, forming a **tetrad** as the chromatin coils.

    b. **Metaphase I:** The homologs align themselves on the center line of the cell.

        i. **Chiasmata** form between nonsister chromatids to prevent the homologs from repelling each other.

        ii. **Crossing over** can occur.

        iii. Results in recombinant chromatids.

        iv. **Sister chromatids** are half of the duplicated chromosome.

    c. **Anaphase I:** The homologs pull apart to opposite ends.

    d. **Telophase I:** The nuclear envelope forms again, and the cytoplasm pinches off.

3. Meiosis II

    a. The DNA is NOT replicated a second time.

    b. Currently have two diploid (2n) daughter cells.

    c. The same thing that happens in meiosis I happens again.

    d. **Prophase II:** Homologous chromosomes pair up.

    e. **Metaphase II:** The homologs align themselves at the center of the cell.

    f. **Anaphase II:** The homologs pull apart, leaving individual chromatids at each pole.

    g. **Telophase II:** The nuclear envelope re-forms, and the cytoplasm pinches apart to form four genetically different haploid (n) daughter cells.

4. There are always errors that can happen.
   a. **Nondisjunction:** The act of the homologous pairs failing to separate.
   b. **Aneuploidy:** When there is an extra or missing chromosome.
      i. **Trisomy:** Three of one type of chromosome.
         1. Trisomy 18 (Edwards syndrome) and 21 (Down syndrome) are the most common.
      ii. **Monosomic:** Only one chromosome.
      iii. **Polyploid:** Refers to more than one set total of chromosomes
         1. We are **diploid** (2n), except for our reproductive cells (sperm and eggs). This means that we have two of each chromosome, one from mom and one from dad. Polyploid would be 3n or 4n.
   c. **Translocation:** Part of a chromosome can break or get caught on another, so when anaphase takes place, a cell has a full set of chromosomes plus a small part of another one.
      i. This can also cause Down syndrome or familial Down syndrome.
5. **Karyotype:** Used to see the number, shapes, and sizes of all the chromosomes in a cell and to determine abnormalities in gametes.


## Section 11.4: Cell death

1. Cell death happens in two specific ways.
   a. Necrosis
      i. Cell is damaged and killed unwillingly by disease.
      ii. If any cell dies from necrosis, it is usually a sign of infection or lack of nutrients.
   b. Apoptosis
      i. Programmed cell death.
      ii. A cell receives a signal to shut down and essentially commit suicide. This happens daily in your body, and you don't even know it.
      iii. An essential process for development; e.g., to form the spaces between fingers and toes.
2. Tumors
   a. Benign
      i. Slow-growing, noncancerous growths that resemble the tissue they came from.
   b. Malignant
      i. Often have very irregular structures due to rapid growth and no longer resemble the tissue they came from.
      ii. Tend to be cancerous.

c. Metastasis
   i. When cancer cells become mobile.
   ii. They can travel through the bloodstream and end up in another part of the body.
   iii. Cells have uncontrolled replication that can damage the body.
d. Oncogene proteins are used as positive regulators for cancer cells.
   i. Stimulate cell division.
   ii. A negative regulator would inhibit the cell cycle.
   iii. When oncogenes get out of control is when we develop cancer. The regulation of the oncogene is no longer in place, and our cells divide uncontrollably whether they are ready or not.
   iv. Frequently control the cell cycle.

# CHAPTER ELEVEN WORKSHEET ACTIVITIES

## Matching

1. ___Metaphase
2. ___Prophase
3. ___Cytokinesis
4. ___Anaphase
5. ___Telophase

A. The cytoplasm divides and pinches off.
B. All homologous chromosomes align in the middle.
C. The homologous chromosomes pull apart.
D. The chromatin condenses into chromosomes.
E. Nuclear envelope forms and chromosomes relax.

## Fill in the blanks

1. Meiosis forms _____ and mitosis forms _____.
2. Mitosis will form two _____ daughter cells.
3. _____ occurs in meiosis and can increase genetic variability.
4. If a cell is starved of oxygen or nutrients, _____ will occur and the cell will unwillingly die.
5. _____ tell the cell when it is OK to proceed to the next step. Without this, the cell with stay in interphase indefinitely.
6. Nondisjunction occurs, and chromosome number 8 fails to separate. The type of ploidy this cell will have would be _____.
7. The microfilament ring in cytokinesis is made out of _____ and _____.
8. The four chromatids of each homologous pair form a(n) _____.
9. The _____ are located on the centromere of the sister chromatids.
10. When the chromatin condenses, it wraps around _____ to help it coil and condense into a chromosomal structure.

Label the diagram

1.

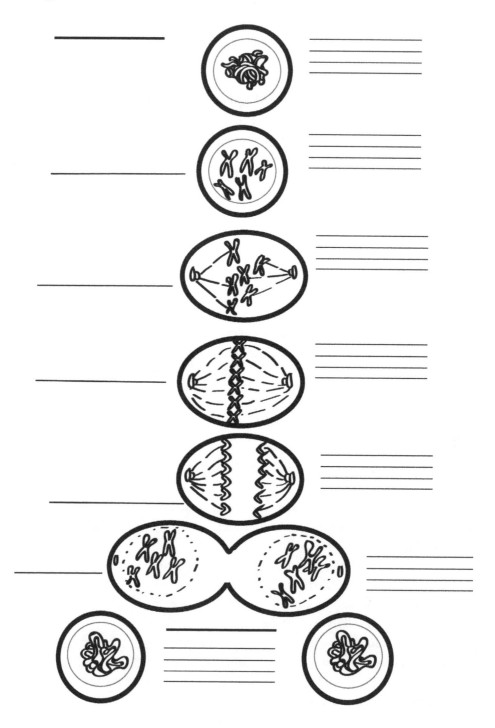

# CHAPTER ELEVEN PENCAST SUMMARY

Below is an outline of the pencast for Chapter 11. To review how to access this pencast, as well as pencasts for future chapters, please refer back to the introduction and read the instructions.

## Chapter Eleven: Cell Division: Meiosis and Mitosis

0–2:30: **Keyword terms**
- Haploid: one complete set (n)
- Diploid: two complete sets (2n)
- 2n = 46 → humans; homologous
- Ploidy: number of chromosome sets
- Homology: likeness in structure
- Chromosome pairs that are approx. the same length, centromere position, and type of gene
- Alleles: gene variants
- Sister chromatids

2:30–4:00: **Cell cycle**
- G1 phase: G = gap, but better to think as "growth" of cell
- Restriction point
- Checks for damage in DNA
- Apoptosis
- S phase: synthesis phase
- G2: more cell growth
- M phase: mitosis

4:00–5:30: **CDKs and cyclin**
- Regulate cell cycle
- Phosphorylates target proteins in cell cycle

5:30–12:00: **Mitosis and meiosis**
- Both involve nuclear division.
- MITOSIS: Asexual reproduction
  - Prophase → start with 2n cells
  - Prometaphase
  - Metaphase
  - Anaphase
  - Telophase

- Cytokinesis: division of cytoplasm following telophase
- Result: two identical diploid cells
- Two 2n cells
- Occurs in somatic cell division
  - MEIOSIS: sexual reproduction
    - Meiosis I:
      - Prophase I → have tetrads unlike mitosis
      - Metaphase I → independent assortment
      - Anaphase I
      - Telophase I
    - Meiosis II:
      - Prophase II →chromosome condense again; NO crossing over; start with two 2n
      - Metaphase II
      - Anaphase II
      - Telophase II → 4n cells; gametes
      - Cytokinesis

# 12

# GENE EXPRESSION

## INTRODUCTION

In Chapter 4 we introduced the concept of gene expression, but we focused almost entirely on nucleotides and their role in the central dogma. In this chapter, we will go into more detail on how a DNA sequence within a gene is copied into RNA (transcription) and how RNA is translated into proteins. We will then need to consider the nuances that make these processes something highly regulated in the cell. Knowing the differences in prokaryotes and eukaryotes will benefit your understanding of this chapter. Eukaryotic mRNA is processed differently than prokaryotic mRNA.

A good starting block for students is to look back at the central dogma introduced in Chapter 4. Begin to think about the differences between mRNA, rRNA, and tRNA and their roles in the central dogma. Apply this thinking to your knowledge about the mechanism in which RNA polymerase transcribes the information encoded in DNA to become a message. You will need to be able to use the table of the genetic code to determine what protein is coded by DNA.

Eukaryotes, prokaryotes, and even viruses all use the process of gene expression. It is essential for a cell's structure and function for there to be regulation of gene expression. The one-gene, one-enzyme experiment helps students understand how gene products work together. The process of protein synthesis is complex, so pay attention as we go into detail about how our genetic code, stored in DNA, is "interpreted" during gene expression, giving rise to an organism's phenotype.

**Study Tip 12.1:** Draw RNA polymerase with DNA coming out as a double helix translating the RNA. Be sure to label the 5' and 3' end.

# TOPICS STUDENTS FOUND CHALLENGING

Students were surveyed just after they took an exam that emphasized the topics in this unit. The areas these students found the most challenging are listed below.

- Transcription and translation processes (80%)
- Difference between mRNA, rRNA, and tRNA (60%)
- Start and stop codons; direction (e.g., N→C, 5'→3') (40%)
- RNA splicing (exons and introns) (35%)
- *Neurospora* (one-gene, one-enzyme hypothesis) (25%)

# CHAPTER TWELVE OUTLINE

## Section 12.1: What is the central dogma?

1. Understand what happens when a gene is broken.
   a. It's a **mutant**, and the organism may or may not live.
2. Mutations
   a. Each gene produces an enzyme or protein. For the majority that produce enzymes:
      i. Each enzyme is required for the next step in a biochemical pathway; be able to explain (**one-gene, one-enzyme experiment**).
      ii. Helps problem solve on where a mutation is occurring (meaning this is how scientists would figure out what the genes do together in a biochemical pathway).
3. **Central dogma** theory
   a. DNA → RNA → protein (See Figure 12.1).
   b. Transcription (DNA → RNA) vs. translation (RNA → protein) (see Section 4.3).
   c. Crucial exception are **retroviruses**.
4. Differences between different types of RNAs.
   a. mRNA: carry the genetic information from DNA to the ribosome.
   b. tRNA: adaptor molecule that helps decode mRNA sequences into proteins.
   c. rRNA: a component of the ribosome that allows for protein synthesis.
   d. snRNA: found in the nucleus and involved in the slicing of RNA.
5. The genetic code sequence can be used to make proteins.
   a. From gene to protein: Be able to draw DNA in the nucleus and how mRNA is produced, processed, and translated in the cytoplasm or the rough ER (RER).

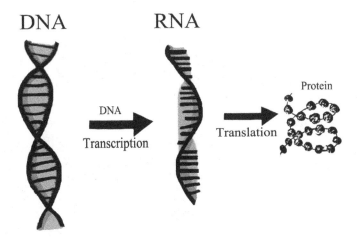

DNA

RNA

Protein

DNA

Translation

Figure 12.1 Transcription/translation, also known as the Central Dogma Theory

## Section 12.2: What is transcription?

1.  **RNA polymerase**
    a.  An enzyme that catalyzes the synthesis of RNA
2.  **Transcription:** DNA → RNA, happens in three steps
    a.  **Initiation:** RNA binds to DNA site called a **promoter** at the initiation site.
    b.  **Elongation:** RNA polymerase unwinds DNA like a telephone cord and reads from 3' to 5' direction (shorthand: 3'–5'), or C terminus to N terminus.
    c.  **Termination:** RNA polymerase reaches the stop codon and is released from the DNA. DNA regains its helix shape.
3.  How is info in DNA transcribed to produce RNA?
    a.  **Triplet codes** of bases (A, T, C, G) called codons account for 20 different amino acids.
    b.  What triplets should you know? **Start and stop codons**
        i.   Start: AUG
        ii.  Stop: UAA, UAG, UGA
    c.  **Aminoacyl-tRNA synthetase:** assists in these enzymes facilitate the binding of the amino acid to the tRNA.
    d.  **Wobble:** When the base at the end of a codon isn't always specific (e.g., CUU, CUC, CUA, and CUG are all leucine). Notice that the first two are the same and the third is different, but they still all code for leucine.

## Section 12.3: What is translation, and how does mRNA code for a protein?

1. **Translation:** RNA → protein
   a. RNA is read **5'–3'** (and proteins are created: **N** terminus to **C** terminus).
   b. The job of the **tRNA** is to transfer (hence the *t*) the amino acid (the "protein building block") to the ribosome to be made into a protein.
      i. If mRNA is the worker constructing the building, the tRNA is the person transporting the bricks (amino acids) to the worker.

## Section 12.4: How and why are genes modified before translation?

1. **Gene splicing**
   a. This happens in eukaryotes, not prokaryotes.
   b. This is how precursor mRNA (pre-mRNA) becomes processed mRNA (mature mRNA).
   c. Exons and introns
      i. **Introns:** the extra information that is spliced out.
      ii. **Exons:** the coding portions in DNA that become processed mRNA.
   d. Splicing also involves the sticking back together of exons so they can code for a protein.
2. **5' cap** and **poly-A tail:** This is still just for eukaryotes.
   a. What role do these play in protein synthesis? How do they protect mRNA?
      i. mRNA makes it so that a message (DNA) lasts as long as it should by protecting it with a 5' cap.
      ii. The length of poly-A tail helps determine the life span of mRNA.
      iii. 5'cap is essential for translation.

## Section 12.5: How do ribosomes allow for translation to happen?

1. **Ribosome**
   a. Has one large subunit and a small subunit.
   b. This is the "workbench" where tRNAs, rRNA as part of the ribosome, and mRNA come together. The ribosome is the bench, since the mRNA is moving through the ribosome, and the tRNAs are coming in, allowing for the protein to be made.
   c. The peptidyl transferase activity of the ribosome forms the new peptide bonds to make the polypeptide.
   d. Ribosome(s) walk along the mRNA strand.
2. **Aminoacyl tRNA synthetases**
   a. These enzymes are responsible for the "second genetic code," since each tRNA needs to be loaded with exactly the right amino acid.

b. tRNA charging requires 20 different aminoacyl-tRNA synthetases, 1 for each of the 20 amino acids.

## CHAPTER TWELVE WORKSHEET ACTIVITIES

## Study Questions

1. What is elongation?
2. What is a release factor?
3. What is a template strand, and where does it come from?
4. Explain wobble—why is it significant?
5. What is the difference between introns and exons?
6. When RNA is translated to protein, what is different comparing translation on the ribosomes in the cytoplasm to the ones located on the rough ER?
7. What are mutagens and mutations? What is an example of a mutagen? What can that mutagen do to the DNA?
8. Define *transcription* and *translation*. What's the difference between the two?
9. What does transcription require? What does it produce?
10. What is a retrovirus, and what makes it unique?
11. Describe how the ribosome translates from RNA to protein.
12. What do RNA polymerases do?
13. Define *codon* and *anticodon*.
14. What are the three phases in transcription?
15. Fill in the table on the following page to understand the four types of RNA.

| TYPE OF RNA | WHAT DOES THE SMALL LETTER STAND FOR? | DESCRIBE ITS ROLE IN TRANSLATION |
| --- | --- | --- |
| mRNA | | |
| tRNA | | |
| rRNA | | |
| snRNA | | |

# CHAPTER TWELVE PENCAST SUMMARY

Below is an outline of the pencast for Chapter 12. To review how to access this pencast, as well as pencasts for other chapters, please refer back to the introduction and read the instructions.

## Chapter Twelve: Gene Expression

**0:00–0:23: Cell communication**
- o Cell communication
- o Cell membrane
- o Transport molecules across the cell wall

**0:24–1:34: Channel receptors**
- o Channel receptors
- o Protein-kinase cascade
- o Intracellular receptors

**1:35–4:12: Protein-kinase receptors**
- o PK receptors
- o What does PK do?
- o How is it working inside the cell?

**4:15–7:33: G-linked protein receptors**
- o G-protein linked receptors

**7:35–8:54: Intracellular receptors**
- o Intracellular receptors

# 13

# DNA AND BIOTECHNOLOGY

## INTRODUCTION

The topic of recombinant DNA and biotechnology has been one of the most enjoyable units that cell biology students engage with, while at the same time being an especially challenging subject to master. The intent of this chapter is to serve as an introduction to recombinant DNA and biotechnology, and thus there are many techniques not discussed here. Today next-generation sequencing (NGS) is one of the more advanced technologies used to understand genomes of multiple organisms at once, an example being the microbiome of the entire gut. To understand how we use these advanced techniques, we need to begin with general recombinant DNA and biotechnology procedures.

Recombinant DNA, on its own, is chimeric DNA molecules formed by cutting and slicing DNA in such a way that foreign DNA or the DNA for a gene of interest is inserted into vectors such as plasmids. Understanding how plasmids work is essential for explaining all the important techniques of recombinant DNA. In short, you want your gene of interest inserted into a plasmid at exactly the right time, using combinations of enzymes to cut and paste DNA. The essential enzymes for this procedure include restriction enzymes and ligase. Plasmids and other vectors are used in a wide range of methods and have specific restriction enzyme sites that allow for the insertion of foreign DNA. These vectors typically have a selectable maker, allowing us to identify the plasmids that have an inserted gene, which in turn tells us which bacteria has the plasmid. While recombinant DNA is mostly explained in bacteria, there is the ability to put these plasmids into other kinds of life, including plants and transgenic animals.

As mentioned earlier, there are a wide range of biotechnology procedures, each used for a specific purpose. Due to the complexity of these procedures, it is best to focus on understanding the procedures introduced at this stage of your biology education, rather than trying to learn all the methods and techniques right now.

## TOPICS STUDENTS FOUND CHALLENGING

Students were surveyed just after they took an exam that emphasized the topics in this unit. The top areas these students found the most challenging are listed below.

- Cloning (recombinant DNA) (60%)
- Reporter genes (40%)
- Genomic and cDNA libraries (37%)
- Expression vectors (35%)

## CHAPTER THIRTEEN OUTLINE

### Section 13.1: What is recombinant DNA?

1. DNA formed artificially.
2. Slicing and recombination of genetic material from multiple sources.

### Section 13.2: How is a recombinant plasmid made? (See Figure 13.1)

1. Plasmids and other vectors allow for foreign DNA to be inserted into specific restriction enzyme sites.
2. The essential enzymes for this procedure include restriction enzymes and ligase.
   a. **Restriction enzymes** cut the DNA at exact sequences of bases in the DNA. They may leave an **overhang** of single-strand DNA, which makes the cloning procedure easier.
   b. **Ligase** is used to bond ("glue") fragments of DNA back together (re-forming the phosphodiester linkages between bases).
   c. The goal is to insert your gene of interest into the plasmid when it is glued back together.
3. These vectors typically have a **selectable marker** that allows us to identify the plasmids that have an inserted gene, which in turn tells us which bacteria has the plasmid.
   a. Antibiotic resistance genes; e.g., ampicillin or kanamycin.
   b. Jellyfish fluorescent proteins (green fluorescent protein = **GFP**) and other visible protein markers.

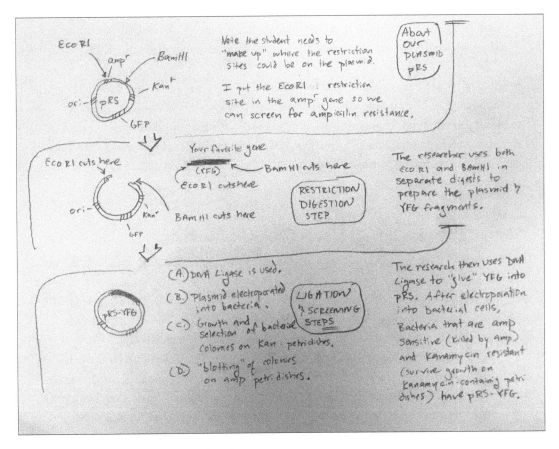

Figure 13.1 How to clone a gene into plasmid

   c. Selectable markers can be broken or used to validate the plasmid is there.
     i. If broken, that might mean your gene of interest has been inserted.
     ii. To clone a gene, the strategy is usually to break one selectable marker to show the gene is probably there before further analysis and to use a different marker to make sure the plasmid is also in the bacteria. So usually plasmids have more than one marker.

4. Expression of a protein from a plasmid is one way to use the plasmid in research. Other research might use the plasmid in a different way; e.g., to analyze the DNA making up "your favorite gene."
   a. GFP is a **reporter gene**, since the DNA is expressed on the plasmid and we observe green bacteria growing on a petri dish or maybe using a microscope if we are using the bacteria in an experiment.
   b. Analysis of the DNA might mean **sequencing** the DNA, so we learn the entire sequence of the DNA bases in the gene. This means we know which base comes first, going 5' to 3' in the DNA.

5. While recombinant DNA is mostly explained in bacteria, there is the ability to put these plasmids into other kinds of life, including plants and transgenic animals.

**Study Tip 13.1:** Draw a plasmid and show the use of restriction enzymes BamHI, EcoRI, and DNA ligase. The plasmid contains ampicillin and kanamycin antibiotic markers and the GFP protein. Draw these features in the plasmid. Using a flowchart or storyboard (series of arrows from one "scene" to the next), show the multiple steps necessary to clone a gene of interest into the plasmid. Please note that both the plasmid and YFG have BamHI and EcoRI in useful places.

## Section 13.3: How are libraries of DNA used in research?

1. Cloning DNA isn't always about only working with "your favorite gene," but instead looking for important genes.
2. Sometimes cloning DNA means making a catalogue of all the DNA in a sample. This would be a complete **genomic library** if it includes all the DNA of an organism.
   a. This allows a researcher to look for a gene of interest in the library.
3. A genomic library may be made of many small plasmids that contain all the genes of viral vectors or certain bacterial vectors that contain larger fragments of many genes.
4. Next-generation sequencing (NGS) strategies are simplifying how we work with entire genomes of information, and the analysis of this information is an important kind of **bioinformatics**: the science of collecting and analyzing complex biological data. Typically, bioinfomaticians have some knowledge of computer science and statistics as well as biology, including genetics.

## Section 13.4: Introduction: some essential biotechnology methods

1. A genomic library can be made from RNA and use the enzyme **reverse transcriptase (RT)** to make a DNA copy of the RNA before cloning into plasmids.
   a. This is an important strategy to learn about what messenger RNA is being expressed in a cell at a center time.
2. The polymerase chain reaction (**PCR**) is a method for amplifying a small amount of DNA to make billions of copies of that particular DNA fragment.
   a. This process uses a machine called a thermocycler to heat and cool the DNA, which is mixed with specific primers that are the starting part of new DNA strands.
   b. If reverse transcriptase (RT) is used in a previous step, the PCR process can be used to make a lot of DNA fragments from the RNA, in a process call **RT-PCR**.

# CHAPTER THIRTEEN WORKSHEET ACTIVITIES

## Study Questions

1. What is recombinant DNA, and how is it used to do research?
2. What is used to cut the DNA into fragments?
3. What bacterium was first used for recombinant DNA technology?
4. Describe the difference between blunt ends and sticky ends.
5. What is the act of transformation?
6. How are selectable marker genes used?
7. How can recombinant DNA be inserted into a cell?
8. What is a plasmid?
9. DNA fragments used for cloning come from four sources. What are these four sources?
10. What is the genomic library? The cDNA library?
11. How is cDNA produced?
12. What are reverse transcriptase and PCR used for?
13. What is the knockout experiment in animals?
14. What does interference RNA (RNAi) do?
15. How is biotechnology beneficial to society?

# CHAPTER THIRTEEN PENCAST SUMMARY

Below is an outline of the pencast for Chapter 13. To review how to access this pencast, as well as pencasts for other chapters, please refer back to the introduction and read the instructions.

## Chapter Thirteen: DNA and Biotechnology

0:00–0:20: **Gene expression**
  o Gene expression
  o Central dogma
  o rRNA, tRNA

0:21–5:00: **RNA polymerase**
  o RNA polymerase
  o RNA polymerase transcribes information in DNA to become a message.
  o An enzyme that catalyzes the synthesis of RNA
  o Initiation

- o Elongation
- o Termination

**5:15–12:13: Ribosomal transcription**
- o Ribosomal transcription
- o The process of transcription
- o RNA is read 5'–3' (N terminus to C terminus)
- o Start codons and stop codons

# APPENDIX

## ANSWERS TO CHAPTER ONE WORKSHEET ACTIVITIES

**Study Questions**

1.  What is cell theory?
    a.  Cell theory is the scientific theory, which describes the properties of the cell, saying that the cells are the smallest basic building blocks of life.
2.  What are the two classification groups for cells?
    a.  Cells are classified as prokaryotes and eukaryotes.
        i.  Prokaryotes do not have a nuclear membrane.
        ii. Eukaryotes are characterized by the presence of the nuclear envelope.
    b.  Prokaryotes are divided in two subcategories (domains)
        i.  Bacteria
        ii. Archaea
    c.  Eukaryotes belong to the Eukarya domain.
3.  How did life arise? What is endosymbiotic theory?
    a.  Biological molecules arose through the random physical interactions of chemicals.
    b.  Endosymbiotic theory, also referred to as symbiogenesis, is the evolutionary theory that describes the origin of eukaryotic cells from prokaryotic ones. Prokaryotes began to live in

close independent relationships, which eventually marked the beginning of eukaryotes.

4. When did photosynthesis occur, and what made it possible?

   a. Photosynthesis occurred approximately 2.5 billion years ago. Photosynthesis is the process of transforming light energy into chemical energy. This process used $CO_2$ from the environment and released $O_2$.

   b. The high levels of $O_2$ in the atmosphere enabled the creation of aerobic organisms, organisms that could tolerate $O_2$. In addition, abundant $O_2$ enabled organisms to grow larger. Another important advantage of $O_2$ is the formation of the ozone layer in the atmosphere, which protected the organisms from UV radiation. The organisms started to leave the water and settled on the land.

5. List the characteristics of living organisms.

   a. Living organisms are made up of macromolecules (carbohydrates, proteins, lipids, nucleic acids).

   b. The building blocks of living organisms are cells.

   c. One of the functions of cells is to convert the molecules obtained from the environment into chemical energy (food for the organism).

   d. Another function of cells is to retrieve energy from the environment in order to do biological work.

   e. Living organisms have genetic information.

   f. Living organisms are able to maintain homeostasis (self-regulate their internal environment).

6. What is the difference between anaerobic and aerobic metabolism?

   a. Anaerobic metabolism does not use $O_2$ to function.

   b. Aerobic metabolism requires $O_2$ in order to function normally.

7. What is a phylogenetic tree, and what is its function?

   a. A phylogenetic tree is a diagram used to portray the differences and similarities between groups of organisms.

8. How are organisms classified?

   a. Earth's organisms are classified by three domains: Bacteria, Archaea, and Eukarya.

9. How do the three domains different from each other?

   a. Archaea and Bacteria are single-celled prokaryotes, while Eukarya are eukaryotic cells (e.g., mitochondria and chloroplasts).

10. What is the difference between a population, a community, and an ecosystem?
   a. A population is a group of organisms that belong to the same species.
   b. A community is the group of all the populations that live in a specific area.
   c. An ecosystem is all communities together with the abiotic elements.
11. What are some ways plants have adapted to the environment?
   a. Plants have adopted traits to protect them against predators such as thorns. They have also adapted traits, which attract other organisms that help in their reproduction (for example, nectar attracts bees).
12. What types of work do cells perform? Explain.
   a. Mechanical work: changing the location of one cell molecule to another, moving the whole tissue or moving the whole organism itself.
   b. Chemical work: synthesis of new molecules from smaller ones (carbohydrates deposited as fats).
   c. Electrical work: neutron processing in nervous system.
13. What is genetic code?
   a. A genetic code encodes all the information related to physical appearance and internal environment.
14. Describe the relationship between evolution by natural selection and the genetic code.
   a. If a genetic code is altered, new proteins will be formed, which will lead to variation. Natural selection will choose the best variation.
15. What is scientific investigation?
   a. A scientific investigation is a method of observation, hypothesis, experimentation, data, and conclusion.
16. What are the parts of scientific investigation?
   a. Make observation
   b. Ask questions
   c. Hypothesis
   d. Make a prediction
   e. Conduct an experiment
   f. Gather data
   g. If results support hypothesis, new study.
   h. If results do not support hypothesis, revise the hypothesis.

17. What is the difference between inductive and deductive logic?
    a. Inductive logic: creating a new proposition based on the observations and facts.
    b. Deductive logic: begins with a hypothesis, which is thought to be true, and then continues to predict what other facts need to be true in order for the hypothesis to be proved true.
18. Differentiate between the two types of experimentation.
    a. There are two types of experimentation, controlled and comparative.
        i. A controlled experiment manipulates one or more variables.
        ii. A comparative experiment compares the end result of the experiment to other sources.
19. What is the difference between prokaryotic and eukaryotic cells?
    a. The main difference between prokaryotic and eukaryotic cells is the presence of the nuclear envelope wrapping the chromosome.

# ANSWERS TO CHAPTER TWO WORKSHEET ACTIVITIES

**Study Questions**

1. How do the charges of protons and electrons affect how atoms interact?
    a. The electrons are the negatively charged particles. The valence electrons determine how reactive an atom will be. Atoms have a tendency to their last valence shells with two electrons in the first shell and eight electrons the second, which is called the octet rule. If an atom does not have two or eight electrons in the outermost valence shell, the atom is unstable and will interact with other atoms until it fills the valence shell. Protons and neutrons are found in the nucleus. Protons are positively charged particles. Protons and neutrons make up the mass number. The number of protons is also called the atomic number, and it determines the chemical properties of an element.

2. What is the relationship between an electron, its orbital, and its electron shells? How are orbitals and electron shells different?
    a. Electrons are in the electron cloud, which can be broken down into levels known as electron shells. In these electron shells it is almost impossible to know where an electron is at any moment; this is where orbitals come into play. Orbitals are a way of describing the volume of space that an electron spends most of its time in. Electron shells and orbitals differ in that orbitals depict an accurate representation of electron configuration, because the shape and position of electrons in space are actually specified, while electron shells are just a convenient way of determining how an atom should react with other atoms based on the valence shell.

3. What is the max amount of electrons located in an orbital? Does this change as the orbitals circle farther away from the nucleus?
    a. The maximum amount of electrons located in an orbital is 2. As the orbitals circle farther away from the nucleus, the amount of electrons changes: in subshell s: 2 electrons, subshell p: 6 electrons, subshell d: 10 electrons, and subshell f: 14 electrons.

4. Why are elements known as "pure"?
    a. Elements are known as pure because they are made of just one kind of atom.

5. What distinguishes different isotopes of an element from each other?
    a. Different isotopes can be distinguished from each other because they have a different number of neutrons.
6. Atomic weight is a concept related to isotopes. How do isotopes' varying masses relate to an element's atomic weight?
    a. The average mass numbers of isotopes in their normally occurring proportions (in a natural sample) is the atomic weight.
7. Are isotopes always stable?
    a. No, isotopes are not always stable. When they are unstable, they decay into other elements and release energy.
8. Under what circumstances are isotopes not stable? Why?
    a. When they give off energy in the form of alpha, beta, and gamma radiation = radioisotopes.

**Matching**
    1. D
    2. E
    3. A
    4. C
    5. B

**Fill in the blanks**
    1. Increased
    2. Valence
    3. Hydrogen bond
    4. Hydrophilic
    5. Positive; loses
    6. Buffer
    7. Electronegativity
    8. Specific heat
    9. Potential
    10. Molarity

# ANSWERS TO CHAPTER THREE WORKSHEET ACTIVITIES

## Study Questions

1.  How do the three types of isomers (structural, optical, and cis-trans) differ?
    a.  Isomers have the same molecular formulas but a different arrangement of atoms. Structural isomers are molecules with the atoms arranged in a completely different order. Optical isomers are two molecules that are mirror images of each other. Cis-trans isomers are geometric isomers. These compounds have subunits attached to two adjacent carbon atoms that share a double bond. When the side chains are on the same side of the double bond, the isomer is referred to as cis, and when the side chains are oriented on opposite sides of the double bond, they are called trans.

2.  How are isomers different than isotopes?
    a.  Isomers are differences in atomic arrangements of the same molecule. Isotopes are two of the same atoms with a different number of neutrons.

3.  What are functional groups?
    a.  Functional groups are specific collections of atoms attached to a molecule and have unique characteristic properties regardless of the molecule. Compounds are often classified based on their functional groups.

4.  What is the process of dehydration synthesis (also called condensation reaction), and what is its importance?
    a.  Dehydration synthesis is the process of polymer building. The bonds formed have different names based on the monomers, and condensation is the process to form all of them. Without dehydration synthesis, we wouldn't be able to form the macromolecules that we need for life.

5.  What are the different functions a protein can perform in a cell?
    a.  Proteins can work as enzymes speeding up reactions, acts as signals (hormones) for physiological changes, bind to RNA to allow for gene expression, and many other things.

6.  What are the bonds between amino acids called?
    a.  Peptide linkages

7.  What's the difference between primary, secondary, tertiary, and quaternary structure?
    a.  The "level" of bonding taking place. In primary structure, the bonds are between the monomers to form polypeptide chains. In secondary struc-

ture, polypeptide chains form hydrogen bonds to each other, forming either a beta pleated sheet or an alpha helix. In tertiary structure, these polypeptide chains form many different kinds of bonds and become even more complexly linked. In quaternary structure, more bonds are formed, and the structure begins to resemble a clump.

8. What's the importance of chaperones?

    a. They repair denatured proteins by helping them fold into their functional state.

9. What's the difference between mono-, di-, oligo-, and polysaccharides?

    a. The number of monosaccharides bonded. In mono, there's only one monosaccharide; in di, there's two; in oligo, there's 3 to 20; in poly, there's more than 20.

10. What are the bonds called between monomers in carbohydrates?

    a. Glycosidic linkages

11. Why is it important that fatty acids be amphipathic?

    a. So that one end can exist in water and the other can bond to polar glycerol.

12. What's the main difference between triglycerides and phospholipids?

    a. The phosphate group

13. What are the four main lipid types?

    a. Carotenoids, steroids, triglycerides, and phospholipids.

14. What's the difference between a saturated and unsaturated triglyceride, and what effect does it have on the structure of the molecule?

    a. The difference is that a saturated triglyceride has no double bond and is therefore more solid (take butter, for example). An unsaturated triglyceride has a double bond and therefore takes a liquid form (an example being oils).

15. Describe each macromolecule by its chemical structure and list some biological functions.

    a. **Proteins** are combinations of 20 amino acids. Each protein contains one or more polypeptide chains of amino acids. This primary structure is connected through peptide bonds between each amino acid. Each polypeptide chain is folded in a particular manner to make the secondary protein structure as an $\alpha$ helix or a $\beta$ pleated sheet, where hydrogen bonds between amino acids form these structures. The tertiary structure is the interactions between the R groups from the amino acids in the secondary structures. The R groups can form disulfide bridges, hydrogen bonds, or ionic attractions that will cause the helix or sheet to fold over on itself. The tertiary structures of the different polypeptide chains interact with each other to create a compact, functional protein. Each tertiary subunit has a structure unique to its chemical composition. Proteins can be used as enzymes to catalyze biochemical reactions, as structural support with cell stability, as a receptor to receive cell signals, or as a transport mechanism to carry substances within the cell. Protein structure can be affected by high temperatures, changes in pH, high concentration of polar molecules, nonpolar solutions, and covalent modification (adding another chemical group to an amino acid).

b. **Carbohydrates** are a line of sugar monomers, or monosaccharides. These monosaccharides are then linked together to form polysaccharides. Carbohydrates consist of a combination of carbon, molecular hydrogen, and oxygen. They have the general formula $C_m H_{2n} O_n$. Carbohydrates are used as energy storage, energy transportation, and carbon skeletons for other molecules. There are different names for different carbohydrates. Monosaccharides bind together through glycosidic linkages. A glycosidic linkage forms through a condensation reaction.

c. **Lipids** are nonpolar hydrocarbons, which means they contain only carbon and hydrogen atoms. They are very weak, but van der Waals forces hold them together. Fats and oils are classified as lipids and are used to store energy. There are four different kinds of lipids that we cover in this lecture: phospholipids, carotenoids, steroids, and triglycerides. Phospholipids are integrated in the membrane and are what make it semipermeable. The head is a hydrophilic phosphate group, and the tails are fatty acid chains. Carotenoids and chlorophylls capture the light energy for plant photosynthesis. Steroids are hormones and vitamins utilized by the body to carry out chemical reactions. Triglycerides consist of 3 fatty acids and 1 glycerol; they are amphipathic – the heads are hydrophilic and the tails are hydrophobic. The fatty acid tails form a bilayer that keeps the inside of the cell separate from the outside of the cell.

16. What are the functional groups of an amino acid?

    a.   Amino group, hydrogen atom, carboxyl group, and an R group.

17. What's the difference between pyrimidine and purine?

    a.   The main difference between pyrimidine and purine is that purines have two rings in their structure and pyrimidines have only one ring.

**Fill in the blanks**

1. Nucleosides
2. Chemical (molecular); structural
3. Condensation; hydrolysis
4. Peptide (bond) linkage
5. Glycosidic linkage
6. 3 fatty acids; 1 glycerol
7. Nucleobase; sugar
8. Uracil; thymine
9. Phospholipids; amphipathic
10. Double; single
11. Hydrogen; R-side chain; amino group; carboxyl group
12. R-side chain
13. Cysteine
14. Hexose; six
15. Hydrogen
16. Plant; cellulase
17. Optical
18. Formed; removed (used)
19. Carbon (C); nitrogen (N)
20. Nonpolar covalent

# ANSWERS TO CHAPTER FOUR WORKSHEET ACTIVITIES

**Fill in the blanks**

1. Monomers of nucleotides
2. Nitrogen-containing base
3. Pentose sugar; nitrogen-containing base

4. Adenine; guanine

5. Thymine (uracil for RNA); cytosine

6. T; C; U

7. Single; double

8. Genome

9. Gene

## ANSWERS TO CHAPTER FIVE WORKSHEET ACTIVITIES

**Study Questions**

1. What is the importance of a cell's surface area to volume ratio?
    a. Surface area does not increase as fast as the volume of a cell, so the size of the cell is limited in order to maintain proper functions. Surface area determines how much can enter and leave the cell, while volume determines chemical activity.

2. What are the main functions of a microscope?
    a. Describe the difference between a light and electron microscope.
        i. A light microscope utilizes visible light and magnifying lenses to examine small objects, while an electron microscope utilizes electron beams to magnify an image. In a transmission electron microscope this image is the internal structure, while in a scanning electron microscope the image is just the surface of a specimen.
    b. Follow up: True/False the plasma membrane is best seen with a light microscope.
        i. False. It is best to use an electron microscope to see the plasma membrane.

3. Explain the composition of the plasma membrane and its importance to the cell.
    a. The plasma membrane is composed of phospholipid bilayer, protein, and carbohydrates. The purpose of this membrane is to limit what can enter and leave the cell in order to maintain homeostasis. It is also important in communication between cells.

4.  Fill out the table (✔) for what structures are found in prokaryotic and eukaryotic cells.

| Structure | Prokaryote | Eukaryote |
|---|---|---|
| plasma membrane | ✓ | ✓ |
| nucleus | | ✓ |
| nucleoid | ✓ | |
| ribosomes | ✓ | ✓ |
| cytoplasm | ✓ | ✓ |
| cytosol | ✓ | |
| cell wall | ✓ | ✓ |
| cytoskeleton | | ✓ |
| mitochondria | | ✓ |
| endoplasmic reticulum | | ✓ |
| flagella | ✓ | ✓ |
| pilli | ✓ | |
| cilia | ✓ | ✓ |

5.  What specialized cell structures are specific to plants? Explain their functions.
    a.  Chloroplasts: allow cell to photosynthesize, which allows the cell to create its own food by converting light energy to chemical energy.
    b.  Vacuole: important for structure, allows for storage of compounds, helps in plant growth.
    c.  Plasmodesmata: the living bridges between each plant cell; small tubes that connect the cells to one another.

# ANSWERS TO CHAPTER SIX WORKSHEET ACTIVITIES

## Study Questions

1. Why would glycoproteins and glycolipids be important in immune responses?

   a. Glycoproteins and glycolipids serve as recognition flags. When disease or abnormality within the cell occurs, it can trigger an immune response such as destruction of the cell, preventing further cellular damage and procreation.

2. Do peripheral proteins depend on integral proteins?

   a. No. Peripheral and integral proteins are two separate types of membrane proteins.

3. What is the function of each cell junction type?

   a. Gap junctions allow for substance passage between cells; for instance, heart cells. Blood needs to pass between the cells, so there must be a space allowing for that. Tight junctions keep substances from passing between cells, such as in the bladder, which shouldn't be able to leak. Desmosomes anchor cells together tightly, allowing for materials to move in the extracellular matrix, but are not strong enough to prevent tearing: Consider the skin. It must be elastic enough to stretch but also allow for moisture between the cells.

4. Is the sodium–potassium pump a uniporter, symporter, or antiporter?

   a. The sodium–potassium pump acts as an antiporter, because it allows sodium to travel in the opposite direction as potassium.

5. Does cell adhesion depend on cell recognition? How?

   a. Cell adhesion is a strengthening of cell recognition. When a cell binds to another cell, known as cell recognition, the bond strengthens, known as cell adhesion. Without cell recognition, cell adhesion would be nonexistent.

6. What is the importance of selective permeability?

   a. Without selective permeability, any material, toxic or beneficial, would be able to enter the cell. Similarly, important materials inside the cell would be able to exit. Without selective permeability, the cell could not function.

7. What is the goal of diffusion?

a.  The goal of diffusion is equilibrium. In diffusion, ions move along their concentration gradient in search of balance between the interior and exterior of the cell.

8.  How do diameter, temperature, and concentration gradient dictate how quickly diffusion can occur?

a.  Diameter of the ion at hand determines how easily it passes through the membrane, and thus the speed at which it diffuses. High temperatures mean more energy for the ions, increasing their speed across the membrane. The concentration gradient is what drives ions to move in the first place: The more skewed the gradient, the more quickly the ion will try to pass.

9.  What would the cell look like if it were hypertonic, isotonic, or hypotonic?

a.  Since *hypertonic* refers to having more solution outside the cell, we can expect hypertonic cells to look shriveled and puckered. *Hypotonic*, meaning less solution outside the cell, would lead it to look bloated or round. *Isotonic*, referring to an equality of solution, would look neither bloated nor puckered, but healthy.

10. What's the relationship between channel proteins and carrier proteins? Are they separate forms of the same process or codependent?

a.  Channel proteins are members of the membrane protein family, meaning they allow for passage of specific ions or materials requiring ATP, whereas carrier proteins bind to substances and quicken their passive transport through the cell. So they are neither from the same process nor codependent: They are part of two entirely different transport mechanisms, active and passive.

11. How do gated channels contribute to cell communication?

a.  Gated channels react to external stimuli, stimuli itself being considered communication between the cell and another bodily component.

12. How do primary active transport and secondary active transport differ in their energy sources?

a.  Primary active transport uses ATP directly, whereas secondary active transport uses the energy generated by primary active transport.

# ANSWERS TO CHAPTER SEVEN WORKSHEET ACTIVITIES

**Study Questions**

1. What are the different secondary messengers, and in what pathways can you find them?

    a. Hydrolysis of $PIP_2$ to $IP_3$ and DAG are found within the same pathway. Another pathway is where $IP_3$ allows the influx of $Ca^{2+}$, which synthesizes NO. cAMP is also a second messenger within the epinephrine pathway.

2. List and describe the four receptors mentioned.

    a. Cytoplasmic receptor

        i. Nonpolar/small ligands can cross the phospholipid bilayer, binding to a receptor in the cytoplasm.

    b. Membrane receptor

        i. Large/polar ligands bind to the extracellular portion of transmembrane receptor; unable to cross the bilayer.

    c. Ion channel receptor

        i. Channels for ions such as $Na^+$, $K^+$, $Ca^{2+}$, $Cl^-$; has its own ligand that binds to these receptors to induce a conformational change.

    d. Protein kinase receptor

        i. Activation of receptors causes protein kinase activity, which catalyzes phosphorylation to change their shape and function.

        ii. G protein–linked receptor.

3. Explain the difference between direct and indirect transduction.

    a. With direct transduction, the signal binding to the receptor initiates a cell response; however, with indirect transduction, a signal still binds to the receptor but initiates a secondary response; e.g., secondary messengers.

4. What is a protein kinase cascade, and how does it amplify a signal?

    a. A protein kinase cascade is when a series of protein kinase receptors phosphorylate, or activate, one another, leading to a cell response. They amplify a signal because at each step each single kinase activates more kinases, leading to a more widespread signal.

**Matching**

1. C
2. A

3. D
4. B

**Fill in the blanks**

1. Polar or hydrophilic; transmembrane receptors
2. Enzyme; phosphate group
3. Phosphorylation
4. Antagonist or inhibitor
5. Secondary messengers

# Drawing activity

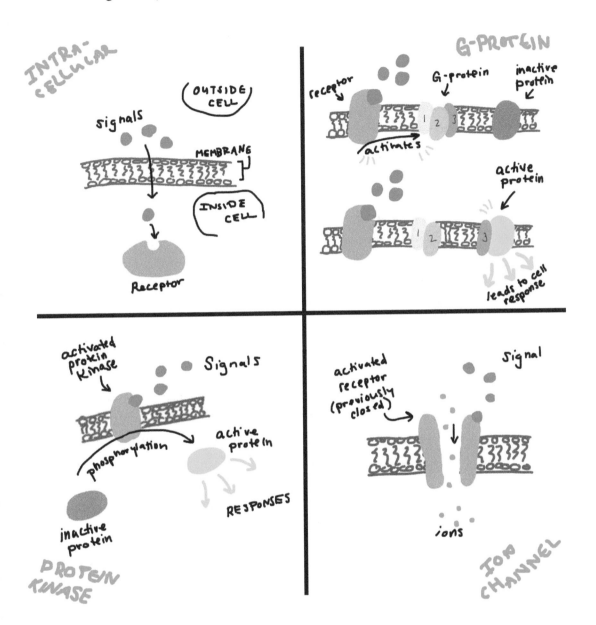

# ANSWERS TO CHAPTER EIGHT WORKSHEET ACTIVITIES

**Short answer**

1. State factors that affect enzyme activity and whether it is affected when increased or decreased.
   a. Temperature, pH, enzyme concentration, substrate concentration, and the presence of any inhibitors or activators.

2. Describe the following terms:
   a. Activation energy: The amount of energy (in joules) required to convert all the molecules in 1 mol of a reacting substance from the ground state to the transition state.
   b. Allosteric regulation: A form of regulation where the regulatory molecule (an activator or inhibitor) binds to an enzyme someplace other than the active site.
   c. Feedback inhibition: Inhibition of an allosteric enzyme at the beginning of a metabolic sequence by the end product of the sequence; also known as end-product inhibition.
   d. Competitive inhibitor: A type of enzyme inhibition reversed by increasing the substrate concentration; a competitive inhibitor generally competes with the normal substrate or ligand for a protein's binding site.
   e. Noncompetitive inhibitor: A noncompetitive inhibitor binds equally well to both free enzyme and the enzyme–substrate complex.
   f. Uncompetitive inhibitor: The reversible inhibition pattern resulting when an inhibitor molecule can bind to the enzyme–substrate complex but not to the free enzyme.

3. Describe entropy and explain how it is related to ΔG.
   a. The extent of randomness or disorder in a system. All chemical reactions are influenced by two forces: the tendency to achieve the most stable bonding state (for which enthalpy, H, is a useful expression) and the tendency to achieve the highest degree of randomness, expressed as entropy, S. The net driving force in a reaction is ΔG, the free-energy change, which represents the net effect of these two factors: $\Delta G = \Delta H - T\Delta S$.

4. List ways to regulate enzyme activity.
   a. Regulatory molecules: Enzyme activity may be turned "up" or "down" by activator and inhibitor molecules that bind specifically to the enzyme.

b. Cofactors: Many enzymes are only active when bound to nonprotein helper molecules known as cofactors.

c. Compartmentalization: Storing enzymes in specific compartments can keep them from doing damage or provide the right conditions for activity.

d. Feedback inhibition: Key metabolic enzymes are often inhibited by the end product of the pathway they control (**feedback inhibition**).

5. Define and list the function of:

a. Coenzyme: Coenzymes are a subset of cofactors that are organic (carbon-based) molecules; e.g., dietary vitamins.

b. Cofactor: A cofactor is an inorganic ion or a coenzyme required for enzyme activity; e.g., DNA polymerase, the enzyme responsible for building DNA molecules, requires Mg2+ to function.

c. Prosthetic group: The non–amino acid part of a conjugated protein is called its prosthetic group; e.g., in hemoglobin or myoglobin, Fe2+ is bound to a prosthetic group called heme.

6. Define *bioluminescence*. List few examples of organisms this is seen in.

a. The biochemical emission of light by living organisms is called bioluminescence; it is observed in fireflies and deep-sea fishes.

## Fill in the blanks

1. Exergonic; endergonic
2. ATP; hydrolysis
3. Lowering
4. Cannot be created nor destroyed
5. Lock and key
6. Induced fit
7. Enzyme–substrate complex
8. Increase
9. Exergonic; negative
10. Coenzymes
11. To the active site
12. Away from the active site
13. Endergonic; positive; exergonic; negative
14. Prosthetic groups
15. Cofactors
16. Cofactor
17. Allosteric regulation

## Label the diagram

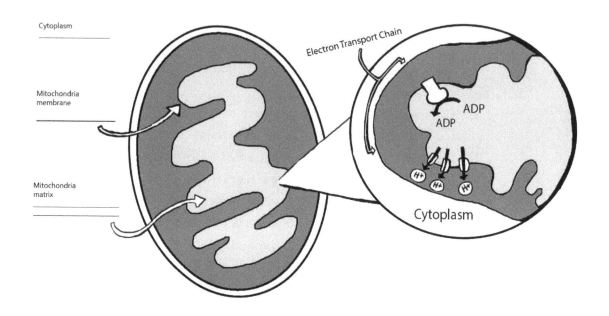

Cytoplasm

Mitochondria membrane

Mitochondria matrix

Electron Transport Chain

ADP

ADP

H+

H+

H+

Cytoplasm

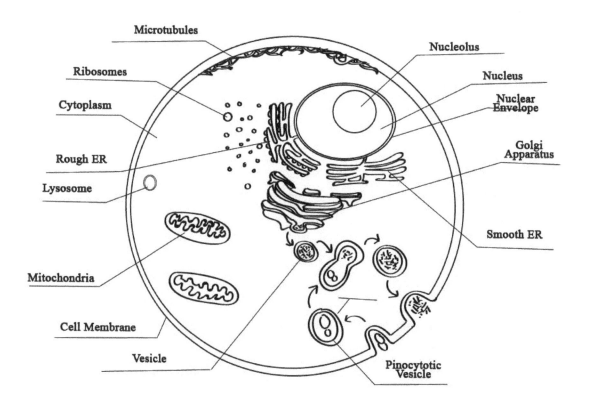

Microtubules

Ribosomes

Cytoplasm

Rough ER

Lysosome

Mitochondria

Cell Membrane

Vesicle

Nucleolus

Nucleus

Nuclear Envelope

Golgi Apparatus

Smooth ER

Pinocytotic Vesicle

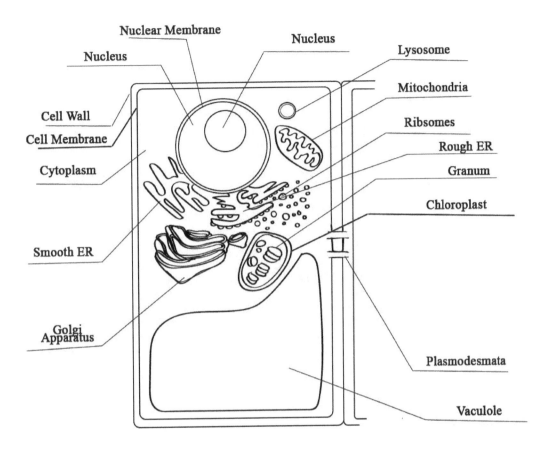

Nuclear Membrane

Nucleus

Nucleus

Lysosome

Cell Wall

Mitochondria

Cell Membrane

Ribsomes

Cytoplasm

Rough ER

Granum

Chloroplast

Smooth ER

Golgi
Apparatus

Plasmodesmata

Vaculole

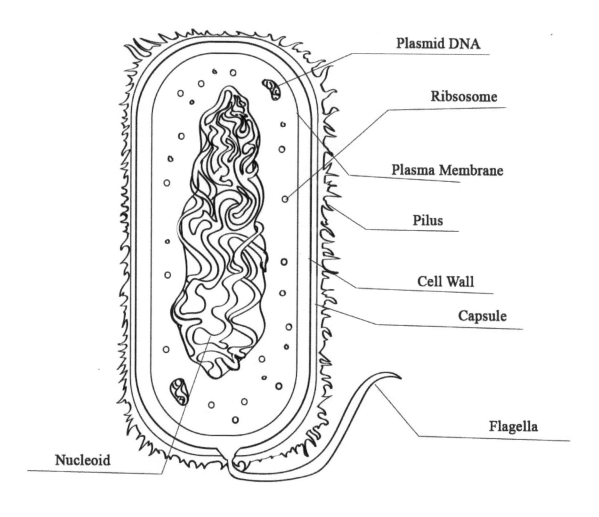

Plasmid DNA

Ribsosome

Plasma Membrane

Pilus

Cell Wall

Capsule

Flagella

Nucleoid

## ANSWERS TO CHAPTER NINE WORKSHEET ACTIVITIES

**Fill in the blanks**

1. Lactic acid; ethanol
2. Loss; gain
3. NAD; FAD
4. Acetyl-coA
5. Chemiosmosis; protons (hydrogen ions)
6. Cytoplasm/cytosol
7. Two

8. Fermentation

9. Chemiosmosis

10. Pyruvate; acetyl-coA

11. Inner membrane of mitochondria; oxidative phosphorylation

12. Substrate-level phosphorylation

13. Two

14. Carbon dioxide

15. Electron transport chain

16. ATP synthase

17. Six

18. Concentration (electrochemical) gradient

19. $F_1$; $F_0$

20. NADH

## Label the following

1.

2.

3.

1) electron transport
2) ATP synthase
3) outer mitochondrial membrane
4) inner mitochondrial membrane
5) Internal Space, (high $[H^+]$) $^+$charge
6) NADH
7) $NAD^+ + H^+$
8) $FADH_2$
9) $FAD + 2H^+$
10) NADH-Q reductase
11) Succinate dehydrogenase
12) Cytochrome C reductase
13) Cytochrome C oxidase
14) $O_2$
15) $H_2O$
16) $ADP + P_i$
17) ATP
18) matrix of mitochondria, Low $[H^+]$ $-$charge.
19) Ubiquinone
20) Cytochrome C
21) respiratory chain
22) oxidative phosphorylation
23) Chemiosmosis, ATP synthase
24) 32+
25) folded inner mitochondrial membrane
26) $F_0$ unit
27) $F_1$ unit

# ANSWERS TO CHAPTER TEN WORKSHEET ACTIVITIES

## Short answer

1. Write down the complete balanced reaction for photosynthesis. State what is reduced and oxidized from the reactants.
   a. Chl + acceptor → Chl$^+$ + acceptor$^-$

i. Chl is the reducing agent; thus,

1) 2ADP +2P;

2) 2 ATP

3) 2 pyruvate

4) 2 NADH

5) 2 NAD⁺

6) 2NADH

7) 2NAD⁺

8) 2 Lactate

9) 2 ATP

10) Lactate dehydrogenase

11) Pyruvate decarboxylase

12) $2CO_2$

13) 2 Acetaldehyde

14) Alcohol dehydrogenase

15) 2 Ethanol

16) 2 ATP

---

1) aerobic

2) fermentation, anaerobic

3) Lactic Acid ⎱ in same
   answer,
4) An alcohol ⎰ interchangeable

5) 2 pyruvate ⎱

6) NADH ⎱ all
   in same
7) 2 ATP ⎰ answer,
   interchangeable

8) enzyme CoA

9) NAD⁺

10) NADH

11) $CO_2$

12) Acetyl-CoA

13) CoA

14) Citrate

15) NAD⁺

16) NADH

17) $CO_2$

18) GDP + P;

19) GTP

20) FAD⁺

21) $FADH_2$

22) $H_2O$

23) oxaloacetate

24) Catabolic

25) exergonic

26) Cytosol

27) mitochondrial matrix

28) exergonic

29) pyruvate, glycolysis

30) pyruvate oxidation

31) aerobic Catabolism

32) Citric Acid Cycle

33) Oxaloacetate is reformed
    glucose molecule,

34) 4, 2, 6, 10

35) Acetyl CoA is the starting Point for the citric Acid Cycle.

36) glycolysis

37) mitochondrial matrix

it gets oxidized (loses an electron).

    ii.   Acceptor molecule is the oxidizing agent; thus, it gets reduced (gains an electron).

2.   Explain the two different types of electron transport systems in mitochondria and chloroplasts.

    a.   Noncyclic electron transport

        i.   Photosystem 1 has $P_{700}$ chlorophyll. It absorbs best at 700nm.

        ii.   Photosystem 2 has $P_{680}$ chlorophyll. It absorbs best at 680nm.

    b.   Cyclic electron transport

        i.   Uses only photosystem 1 and electron transport to produce ATP instead of NADPH.

3.   What does it mean for a plant to be photoautotrophic—what is the significance of this?

    a.   Photoautotrophic plants have the ability to utilize light energy to produce organic molecules. This allows plants to feed themselves and other living organisms. Photosynthesis is also responsible for the $O_2$ in the air we breathe.

4.   List the primary $CO_2$ acceptors, as well as the $CO_2$ fixing enzyme in C3, C4, and CAM plants.

    a.   In C3 plants the primary $CO_2$ acceptor is RuBP and the fixing enzyme is RuBisCO. In both C4 and CAM plants, the primary $CO_2$ acceptor is PEP, and the fixing enzyme is PEP carboxylase.

## Fill in the blanks

1.   $CO_2$; $H_2O$; sugar; $O_2$

2.   Granum

3.   Stomata

4.   Xylem

5.   Stroma

6.   Thylakoid membrane

7.   $P_{680}$ (PhotosystemII); $P_{700}$ (PhotosystemI); electron transport chain

8.   ATP; NADPH

9.   Ferredoxin

10. Water

11. Reduction; oxidation

12. Calvin or carbon fixation stage

13. RuBisCO

14. Six
15. C3

**Draw and label the following**

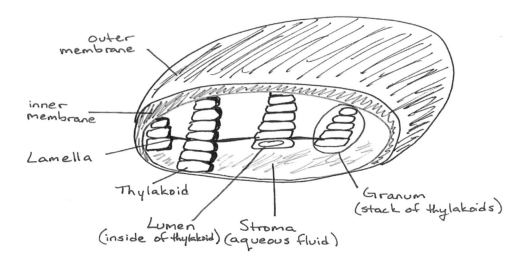

Structure of a Chloroplast

outer membrane
inner membrane
Lamella
Thylakoid
Lumen (inside of thylakoid)
Stroma (aqueous fluid)
Granum (stack of thylakoids)

## ANSWERS TO CHAPTER ELEVEN WORKSHEET ACTIVITIES

**Matching**

1. B
2. D
3. A
4. E
5. C

**Fill in the blanks**

1. Gametes; somatic cells
2. Identical
3. Crossing over
4. Necrosis

5. Cyclin-dependent kinases (CDKs)

6. Trisomy

7. Actin; myosin

8. Tetrad

9. Kinetochores

10. Histones

## Label the diagram

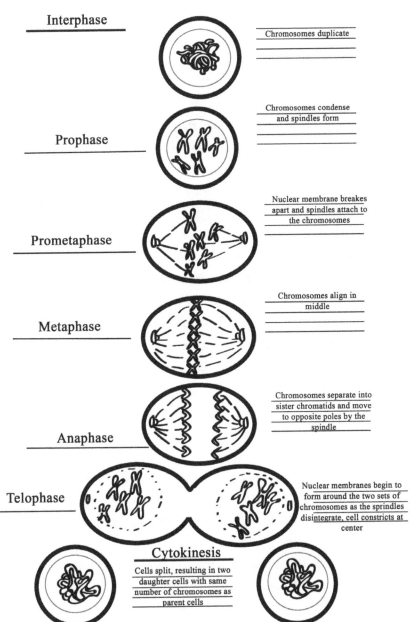

Interphase
_____

Chromosomes duplicate
_____
_____

Prophase
_____

Chromosomes condense
and spindles form
_____
_____

Prometaphase
_____

Nuclear membrane breakes
apart and spindles attach to
the chromosomes
_____

Metaphase
_____

Chromosomes align in
middle
_____
_____

Anaphase
_____

Chromosomes separate into
sister chromatids and move
to opposite poles by the
spindle

Telophase
_____

Nuclear membranes begin to
form around the two sets of
chromosomes as the sprindles
disintegrate, cell constricts at
center

Cytokinesis

Cells split, resulting in two
daughter cells with same
number of chromosomes as
parent cells

# ANSWERS TO CHAPTER TWELVE WORKSHEET ACTIVITIES

## Study Questions

1. What is elongation?
   a. One strand of DNA is used as a template for RNA synthesis. RNA polymerase uses complementary base pairing with the template DNA to create a copy of RNA. This is translation and is an extension of the polypeptide.

2. What is a release factor?
   a. This is a necessary factor (a protein) that binds the stop codon in the mRNA, causing translation to end and the ribosome to release the mRNA.

3. What is a template strand, and where does it come from?
   a. The template strand refers to the sequence of DNA that is copied during the synthesis of mRNA. This is not to be confused with the coding strand, which has the base sequence that directly corresponds to the mRNA sequence that will be translated into protein.

4. Explain wobble—why is it significant?
   a. A wobble base pair is a pairing between two nucleotides in RNA molecules—between mRNA and the tRNA—that does not follow the Watson–Crick rules during translation. Our bodies have a limited amount of tRNA available, so wobbles allow for more efficient use of charged tRNA molecules (tRNA carrying amino acids). Wobble happens in the third base of the mRNA codon; e.g., AAA and AAG both code for the amino acid lysine.

5. What is the difference between introns and exons?
   a. During the process of transcription in a eukaryotic cell, the pre-mRNA is spliced so that it only contains exons. So the introns are spliced out to form the mature mRNA.

6. When RNA is translated to protein, what is different comparing translation on the ribosomes in the cytoplasm to the ones located on the rough ER?
   a. In both cases translation is the same, but the proteins are positioned in the cell differently. The ribosome is actually two different parts (large subunit and small subunit) that only join when the ribosome is active in the translation of mRNA. Translation in the RER packages the proteins in vesicles for transport.

7. What are mutagens and mutations? What is an example of a mutagen? What can that mutagen do to DNA?

a. A mutagen damages DNA. An example could be chemicals or radiation. Mutagens may cause some proteins to be malformed or not functional, thus affecting metabolic pathways within an organism. Mutagens may cause insertions, deletions, and translocations in chromosomal DNA, which can be lethal to the cell.

b. A heritable genetic mutation is a change in DNA that is expressed in the parent and can be passed down to the offspring. An example is blue eyes. Originally, hominids all had brown eyes. A mutation occurred that caused offspring to have blue, green, or hazel eyes. This mutation was neither favorable nor unfavorable and was passed down to later generations. The gene became more widespread in the population, and now we have a large number of people with green or blue eyes.

8. Define *transcription* and *translation*. What's the difference between the two?
   a. Transcription is when the DNA is copied into RNA. We can think of the DNA as the author and the RNA as the TRANSCRIPT the author is writing.

   b. Translation is when the RNA goes to the ribosome to be read. In other words, the ribosome is translating what the author (the DNA) wrote so that the cell can understand it.

9. What does transcription require? What does it produce?
   a. Transcription requires functional DNA, ribonucleotide triphosphates for energy, and an RNA polymerase to do the transcribing.

   b. Transcription will produce the three kinds of RNA we spoke of earlier: mRNA, tRNA, and rRNA.

10. What is a retrovirus, and what makes it unique?
    a. Retroviruses use reverse transcriptase to make DNA out of RNA.

11. Describe how the ribosome translates from RNA to protein.
    a. Translation steps include, in this order: initiation, transcription, and translation. Charged tRNAs enter the ribosome, and peptidyl transferase activity allows the polypeptide to grow in length before the process is terminated.

12. What do RNA polymerases do?

    a.   These create RNA transcripts from the DNA.

13. Define codon and anticodon.

    a.   Each RNA codon is three base pairs long and codes for a specific amino acid. For example, AUG is the start codon.

    b.   An anticodon is the complementary part of a codon, found on a tRNA molecule. So if the codon is AUG, then the anticodon is UAC, and a charged tRNA will carry methionine for addition to the polypeptide.

14. What are the three phases in transcription?

    a.   Initiation, elongation, and termination.

15. Fill in the table to understand the four types of RNA.

| TYPE OF RNA | WHAT DOES THE SMALL LETTER STAND FOR? | DESCRIBE ITS ROLE IN TRANSLATION |
|---|---|---|
| mRNA | messenger | The sequence to be read and matched to become a protein |
| tRNA | transfer | Has the specific anticodon to complement the mRNA strand |
| rRNA | ribosomal | Holds the mRNA in place in the ribosome so that tRNA can match correctly to its complement |
| snRNA | small nuclear | Helps in the process of pre-mRNA splicing and processing |

## ANSWERS TO CHAPTER THIRTEEN WORKSHEET ACTIVITIES

**Study Questions**

1. What is recombinant DNA, and how is it used to do research?
   a. Recombinant DNA is usually made in a lab using two different strands of DNA from different hosts. An example of a recombinant DNA would be extracting the bioluminescence protein from a jellyfish and inserting it into a goldfish's DNA to see whether that protein will be expressed.
2. What is used to cut the DNA into fragments?
   a. Restriction enzymes and DNA ligase.

3. What bacterium was first used for recombinant DNA technology?
   a. *E. coli*
4. Describe the difference between blunt ends and sticky ends.
   a. Sticky ends for DNA is like an overhang on one of the strands. Sticky ends will allow two DNA strands to attach and stick much more easily, like they're Lego blocks.
   b. Blunt ends do not stick together as well, and they're a clean break between two strands of DNA. There is no overhang involved, and it's slightly harder to make these two ends stick back together.
5. What is the act of transformation?
   a. Transformation is the uptake of naked DNA from the environment.
6. How are selectable marker genes used?
   a. When a plasmid is introduced to a group of cells, selectable marker genes are used to determine which cells have uptaken new DNA and become recombinant.
7. How can recombinant DNA be inserted into a cell?
   a. Cells can be treated with chemicals to make the membrane more permeable.
   b. Short electric shocks form pores in the cell membrane to allow DNA to enter.
   c. Viruses and bacteriophage.
   d. Injection into the nuclei of fertilized eggs.
8. What is a plasmid?
   a. A free-floating, self-replicating, double-stranded DNA.
9. DNA fragments used for cloning come from four sources. What are these four sources?
   a. Gene libraries, reverse transcription from mRNA, products of PCR, artificial synthesis or mutation of DNA.
10. What is the genomic library? The cDNA library?
    a. The genomic library is all of the DNA fragments that compose the genome of an organism. So it's every little bit of DNA, regardless of whether those genes are active or inactive.

b. The cDNA library is smaller sections of the genomic library. If the genomic library is an actual library, then the cDNA is like a book being checked out. This "book" is usually a strand of mRNA that is going to be expressed.

11. How is cDNA produced?

    a. With reverse transcriptase.

12. What are reverse transcriptase and PCR used for?

    a. They are used to create and amplify a specific cDNA sequence. They are also used to study expression of certain genes in organisms. A researcher can use these to isolate a specific gene.

13. What is the knockout experiment in animals?

    a. Studying the effects of genes by inactivating them.

14. What does interference RNA (RNAi) do?

    a. Block translation.

15. How is biotechnology beneficial to society?

    a. It allows us to use living cells to produce useful materials. Examples include making some synthetic materials from the same components of spider silk, making beer from yeasts, using bacteria in yogurt and cheese products to increase the probiotics in our guts, and using microbes to produce antibiotics (e.g., penicillin).

    b. It has also helped with the genetic modification of foods. Genetic modification is not bad for our crops, although some people may not want to eat genetically modified foods. We've learned to select or add particular genes in order to grow a plant a certain way. For example, with cabbages, we select for a bigger leafy bud, producing large cabbage heads.

    c. It is also used to adapt plants to the environment. It has helped us grow some crops in lower nitrogen levels and make the crops last for longer periods.

# ABOUT THE AUTHOR
# AND CONTRIBUTORS

Dr. Reid Schwebach is a faculty member of the Department of Biology, coordinator of High School Outreach and Recruitment for the College of Science, and coordinator of the Governor's School at Innovation Park, a dual-enrollment public high school at Mason. He is a founding member of the award-winning Accelerator Program at Mason, which has the goal to support College of Science undergraduate student learning, achievement, and career success. Dr. Schwebach received his PhD in microbiology and immunology from the Albert Einstein College of Medicine. He also holds EdM (secondary science education) and MA (international education development) degrees from Teachers College, Columbia University. He grew up on a farm in New Mexico and has a BA in agriculture and a BS in biochemistry from New Mexico State University. Before coming to Mason, he worked for the Board on Science Education at the National Research Council as a program officer and study director. From 2007 to 2008 he was an American Association for the Advancement of Science–sponsored Science and Technology Policy Fellow at the National Science Foundation, in the Division of Research and Learning. In the New York City public school system, he taught high school chemistry and independent student research at the Beacon School, where he was a principal intern. His scientific research focused on the immunology of *M. tuberculosis*, the bacterial pathogen that causes tuberculosis. He currently works with undergraduate and graduate researchers to investigate the evolution of microbes and to improve how undergraduate students learn science at the university.

Lauren Buchanan is a junior bioengineering major at George Mason's Volgenau School of Engineering. Lauren is currently a lab assistant and technical assistant at the school of engineering and an active member of the Biomedical Engineering society. Lauren has contributed to this book by answering study questions, writing and editing introductions, as well as writing and editing outlines. Lauren wants to go to graduate school to do research and development on artificial hearts, but first she wants to travel the world to see where her interests and expertise are most needed.

Arba Cecia is a pre-health student majoring in neuroscience. She is the coauthor of two scientific papers and has collaborated with mentors in Albania to conduct research in establishing a connection between stroke and sleep-disordered breathing. She was a learning assistant for three semesters for a cell biology class and is a biology research assistant. The learning assistant experience has served her to better understand where students struggle. She helped write the outlines, format the chapters, and made sure new techniques were used to better explain difficult concepts. She plans to go to medical school and become a neurosurgeon as well as a researcher.

Mimi Fuerst is a 2016 Mason alumni and a Fall 2014 graduate of the Smithsonian–Mason School of Conservation. She earned her degree in integrative studies with a concentration in conservation studies and a minor in art and visual technology. After graduating, she became the summer conservation education assistant with the Nature Conservancy's Mashomack Preserve and is currently the teaching assistant for the Smithsonian–Mason School of Conservation's undergraduate program. She was a learning and research assistant for BIOL 213 Cell Structure and Function for the 2015–2016 school year and wrote several of the chapter outlines and designed activities for the book. She hopes that this book will clear up the same common misconceptions she had when taking the course in Spring 2014!

Dana Ismail is a junior at George Mason University pursuing a degree in biology and a minor in Arabic. She has been working as a learning assistant for cell biology—the course that this textbook is aimed toward, for 1 year. Using her knowledge as a learning assistant, Dana worked alongside the other members to help assemble and organize the book, as well as aid in writing and creating schedules for the other team members. With a goal to pursue a future in studying and learning about pathology, Dana hopes that after this experience, she will gain a better foundation in understanding the differences between normal and abnormal cell structures and functions and use it to deepen her understanding of pathology.

Fareshta Jan is a senior in biology honors with premedical track. She is a research assistant for the Office of Student Scholarship, Creative Activities, and Research, and she assisted in creating end-of-chapter questions to help students evaluate their learning method. She also created additional activities in this text by capturing tips from various book contributors who shared their helpful suggestions in order to ace the course. She hopes to provide helpful guidance on understanding the basic fundamentals of cellular biology for both academic and personal benefit.

Athena Kalyvas graduated from George Mason University in December 2016. Prior to George Mason, she attended Northern Virginia Community College, where she got her associate's degree in biology. During her studies there, she participated in the NCAS Community College Scholars program with NASA before graduating and going to Mason. For the past 2 years at Mason, she has worked with Dr. Schwebach on various projects, including being his learning assistant for cell biology lectures. She was also the coordinator for the 17th annual Chesapeake Bay Bowl, a marine biology competition for high school students. She has helped do research on teaching methods and has contributed to the book with her review questions and techniques. After graduation she hopes to become a clinical scribe at the local hospital, INOVA, and attend medical school.

Moonisha Rahman is a rising junior majoring in information technology. She is a research assistant for the Office of Student Scholarship, Creative Activities, and Research, and she helped create the diagrams, figures, and animations, as well as design the book template, layout, and textbook cover. She hopes to utilize her skills to help future students understand difficult concepts and ideas by creating technologically rich tools that benefit learning.

Lauren Smith is a junior majoring in bioengineering at George Mason's Volgenau School of Engineering. While at George Mason, Lauren has worked in the microfluidics lab at the Krasnow Institute for Advanced Studies performing funded research focused on single cell analysis, microfabrication, and micropatterning techniques. She became a research assistant for the Office of Student Scholarship, Creative Activities, and Research, working with Dr. Schwebach to help create resources for the Biology Department's bioinformatics concentration. Lauren is an active member of the Biomedical Engineering Society and the Tau Sigma Honors Society. Lauren's passions include tissue and genetic engineering, where she hopes to focus her research career on the 3-D printing of organs.

Yohanna Tesfaye is currently working as a medical scribe at Memorial Hermann Hospital in Houston, Texas. She recently took the MCAT and will be applying to medical school this coming year. Yohanna graduated from Temple University in 2014 with a bachelor's of science in public health. She then went on to George Mason University to complete a post-bac for medical school. It was there that Yohanna began to work with Dr. Schwebach as a learning assistant for cell biology. She had the opportunity to work with his students and better understand what aspects of the class needed improvement to further their comprehension of the course. This allowed her to work with the team when writing different chapters and activities, keeping in mind how to best address the students and enhance their knowledge.

Mariam Talib is a rising senior at Mason; she is majoring in psychology with a minor in neuroscience and a concentration in industrial and organizational psychology. As a cell biology student, Mariam worked with the LAs and engaged in several independent study activities that we consulted her about to create this book. She has helped assemble the book and has contributed essential components of several chapters; she especially assisted with activities and unit introductions. She offered an important perspective that nonbiology majors bring to this book.

Tess Van Horn is a prehealth sophomore at George Mason University majoring in neuroscience. She interned at Brudnick Neuropsychiatric Research Facility over the summer of 2016 and is currently a learning assistant for cell biology. Tess is also a brother in Alpha Phi Omega and a member of the Honor Committee. She helped in the creation of this book by editing chapters, formatting pages, and testing the material with her students. Tess hopes to graduate May 2018 and begin medical school.

Jennifer Young brings a slightly different perspective to *Cell Structure and Function*. She is a graduate of George Mason University who began her studies in pursuit of a career in international affairs. Along the way, she realized her passion for global health and is now completing her premedical course work as a postbaccalaureate at Rutgers University–New Brunswick. As a nontraditional student, she offers the perspective of a formerly self-proclaimed "nonscience" person. Her premedical studies introduced her to Dr. Schwebach while enrolled in his cellular biology course at Mason. Her contributions to *Cell Structure and Function* pertain, in particular, to the science of learning, as well as being a contributing editor to cellular biology content.

CPSIA information can be obtained
at www.ICGtesting.com
Printed in the USA
BVHW051758231118
533785BV00007B/175/P